To

This is written
from the heart —

I hope you
enjoy it.

All the best,

Peter Walker

MUMBO JUMBO
&
BANANA PEPPERS

MUMBO JUMBO
&
BANANA PEPPERS

Heartfelt Classroom Teaching
and Creative Math Instruction

Peter J. Wilson

NLA
Books

To all of my students over the years.
They've gone along with some crazy
methods and have been dedicated,
courageous, forgiving, helpful and sweet.
They have blessed me more
than they will ever know.

Table of Contents

Foreword

In 1996, Dr. Richard Carlson published a book titled *Don't Sweat The Small Stuff* that went on to occupy top rankings on many major booklists across the world. Peter J. Wilson, the author of this book, sweats the small stuff on a daily basis! That's because he is driven and strives for excellence in his teaching. But he is more than a dedicated teacher. He is a brother, a son, a lover of national parks, a former student of mine, as well as my daughter's former math teacher. Mr. Wilson sweats the small stuff because he really has found his passion in becoming a teacher. He strives to be the best teacher he can be, providing students with rigor, relevance and relationships. Although I believe the reader will be hard-pressed to find Mr. Wilson using the verbiage of "the three R's" in this book, I do believe you will see great examples of them in the stories and anecdotes that follow.

Many of you who have picked up this book are about to enter the teaching profession, or are considering a career change into the field of education, and may be in need of some insight or encouragement related to your decision. Others may be reading because you were drawn to the title. Regardless of how you have arrived here, *Mumbo Jumbo and Banana Peppers* draws on the thoughts and experiences of one man who took a chance at changing his career midstream. And the children and parents of Wisconsin thank him for becoming an educator! I have had the pleasure of seeing students experience "aha" (or gong) moments in his class. I have watched him create a nonprofit from scratch, based on his love of photography and travel. I have also watched Mr. Wilson step out of his comfort zone and delve into the arena of acting. And along the way, I have learned new and creative ways to understand the mathematical world, all thanks to one man's passion for making learning relevant.

At the end of my college classes, I always ask students "What will you take away from today's session?" Well, my take away from *Mumbo Jumbo and Banana Peppers* is that it is possible to transform your life, and with that transformation come benefits that can change the world. Maria Montessori changed many lives. So did Jaime Escalante. Peter Wilson has been changing the lives of young people in his community ever since he decided to find his calling as a teacher. Obviously by looking at the list above, I have placed him in great company! But, then again, both of the aforementioned individuals were teachers that had great impact. If you are about to enter the field of education, are unhappy in your current situation, or if you are wondering where to find your passion, reading this book will change your perspective. I hope you will do what Mr. Wilson did and reach out, explore, be courageous and follow your heart! Maybe you too will add your name to the list of great teachers who have made a difference in their communities!

Corey Thompson, EdD
Assistant Professor, Cardinal Stritch University
Vice President, Imaginaction, Inc.

Preface

"Mr. Wilson, you're full of crazy."
Alexa, 4th grader

When I heard the quote above, I was thrilled. It meant Alexa was engaged in what was going on in the classroom. Now, not all of my teaching gets that kind of reaction, but if you asked my students, most would say they've seen that side of me at one time or another. And that's okay with me.

That's because I am one of the few people who have been lucky enough to find their calling. That calling has allowed me to be "crazy" again: playful and joyful, yet focused and determined to have my students learn more than they ever imagined they could in a classroom.

My journey to teaching is an utter reversal of fortune for a man who thought his life had been wasted. The journey helped me find the passion in my life. This is the story of the lessons learned in the midst of that journey and the effects of applying that passion to the teaching and learning that occur in my classroom.

For many years, I was one of those lost souls in the world of making money to survive, not one of the blessed souls who had found what he was meant to do. Now that I've found teaching, I want to yell at the top of my lungs, "It can be done! Go for it!"

It has been so humbling, and the gratitude I feel is almost indescribable.

After choosing to enter the educational certification process and becoming a new teacher at the age of forty, I thought I had at least somewhat of a grasp on how to teach. During the first years in my new career, it became apparent I had a whole lot more to learn. Now, most of the way I teach has been molded by being in a classroom full of students, with a foundation based on my time in the certification process in college. On-the-job training for teachers is priceless, painful, fun and never-ending. This inside-the-classroom training is the basis for this book; it forced me to rethink my philosophy and has sparked my heart to come alive to create a unique environment for learning in my classroom.

First as a fourth through sixth grade classroom teacher and then as the Math Teacher Leader at an urban school in Milwaukee, I honed my craft to be unusual on purpose. The last thing I wanted was my students thinking learning is boring and useless. On the contrary, I wanted them to be excited to come to school and to love learning. Although some of my methods may be unusual, the results from students and affirmations from parents have told me I need to share my heart and my approach to teaching and learning, to help other teachers and students.

After walking down to a quiet art room to remind
a student with diabetes to eat her afternoon snack:
Me (whispering): *"It's so quiet down here."*
Student: *"It's because we save our loudness for you!"*

Sophie, 4th grader

Let me share how surprises and on-the-job training can be a gift to teachers, even if they are a bit embarrassing. I thought the first week at a new school was a prime chance to show students that field trips could be a part of the school year. Some people said I was crazy, and maybe I was. Being new to the school, starting with a set of fifth graders who may not have had the best classroom behavior, I knew it might be a challenge. But at the same time, taking a field trip would give me a chance to show them I trusted them enough to handle things.

On the day of the trip, several students and I carried boxes of bag lunches from the bus through the gate of the complex to set them down on picnic tables. Several more times we were asked to move the boxes to different tables, and each time I had to bend down to pick up a box. Each time I bent down, I kept feeling a breeze on my thighs. Of course, trying to be discreet, I checked the zipper of my jeans without looking down. Every time I blindly reached down to check, it was zipped up. After forty-five minutes of this nonchalant action, I finally decided it was time to look down. To my astonishment, my pants' zipper was up—but there was a fifteen-inch rip in my jeans up the inseam! Yep, I'd been walking around the complex with fifteen students for forty-five minutes with a huge hole in my jeans. If any of my newly acquired students noticed it, they didn't say anything—they were probably in too much shock to know what to say!

Solution? After "flashing" my dilemma to some giggling co-workers (who offered no help at all), I walked to the first aid station, where several emergency workers got a kick out of my "emergency." They let me use a first aid room to safety pin my pants back together. Luckily, I also had a windbreaker tied around my waist, which from that point on was rotated so it mostly hung in front to hide my safety pins, and my unexpected rip.

Now, if I hadn't felt the deep need to change careers, would I have had the chance to have *that* experience?! This experience is a perfect analogy for my teaching career. In the midst of doing what I love—teaching students and seeing their enthusiasm for life—things may not go the way I planned. But that doesn't mean my vision for student learning ever changes. No, the unpredictability of working with children lends itself to the kind of classroom environment I want: flexible, yet structured; fun, yet rigorous.

If you are reading this book as you enter the teaching profession, know that it is written to help you become a great teacher for your students—guiding them to be curious, challenged, interested, active and engaged learners. I want to help you become a teacher that blows kids away by how much fun they can have in class, while still achieving deep understandings.

If you are reading for another reason, I hope my story of a change of heart and reinvigorated enthusiasm for life will be a spark for you to go after what you have wanted to do. In my own life journey, I *had* to make the change; my life was lost if I didn't. If you are in the same boat, maybe this is the time to change.

The biggest thing I ask of you is to be open to really thinking outside your comfort zone, in a fun, creative way. I guarantee your life will be richer if you come from the best part of you—your heart and soul.

MUMBO JUMBO
&
BANANA PEPPERS

Introduction

"There is no way I'm on earth to do this!" As tears streamed down my cheeks, day after day, I knew there had to be more to life than sitting in front of a computer, writing about a machine that spit out radiator tubes. "Do you actually think I care about this stuff? C'mon, this can't be what I'm here for!"

After seeing my watery, solemn eyes while eating breakfast in the company cafeteria, a co-worker asked what was wrong. I couldn't explain to her, or to anyone, the despair of feeling useless, like I was wasting my talent; I didn't know how to tell her that I *knew* I had more to offer the world. I was wasting something in me, not necessarily knowing what that something was. But I knew I needed something with more heart in it. To me, the corporate world had little or no heart—at least, not the kind of heart I had or wanted to share with the world.

An adult classmate in my first education class,
recounting why she decided to change careers in mid-life:
*"I didn't want to base the rest of my life on a decision
I made when I was eighteen years old."*

When I entered college at eighteen, I had no idea what I wanted to do with my life, so I worked toward getting a business degree with an emphasis on information systems. I thought it would help me get a job, and I could make some money. But I never liked either business or computer programming while in the programs at school. I finished my degree in these areas only because it would help me get out of college as quickly as possible, since my parents were paying for my education.

After graduating in May of 1986, I lived with my parents while looking for a job. That summer, while I acted like I was trying to find a job, I painted the house and watched Cubs' baseball games. Finally, in early October, I landed a computer programming job with a consultant working for Milwaukee Area Technical College. My first day wearing a suit and tie began with my boss leading me to the basement of a building, sitting me down with a tableful of binders, and saying, "Start reading these." The rest of the day was meaningless—and a good glimpse of the grind I'd gotten myself into. The next morning, I sat down to read more binders, and didn't turn a page for two hours. For those two hours, I stared at the pages as I pondered whether I could stay there and what would happen if I quit. I finally approached my new boss and told him the job wasn't for me. He was shocked and said, "You've only been here for two days!" He suggested I give it until Christmas and offered to let me take a walk alone outside to re-think the decision. But I knew; this path was not for me.

When I left the job that morning, I stopped at a mall to apply for a job at a shoe store, and then made my way to a friend's house. Since my dad was working out of the house, and my mom wouldn't be home from her job until after lunch, I waited to go home. At the time, I didn't get along with my dad very well. When I finally did go home and entered the kitchen door, my mom met me with, "What are you doing home?" I told her I quit the job, which my father heard from the other room. You can imagine his response. We got into a shouting match as I broke down crying and spilled my guts of all the thoughts and pains in my heart and soul. It was the first time I had ever opened up to my dad. And it was a benchmark day for me, finally opening up to loved ones about what was really going on inside me. But although it was a benchmark day, I still had to figure out what I was going to do from there. After working for a department store during the holiday season, I finally got another job just to survive, this time as an assistant manager of a finance company.

Two months after starting the finance job, a sports injury altered my life for good. Throughout high school and college, my ego had tricked me into basing much of my self-confidence on my ability to play sports. From being my high school's most valuable player in volleyball, a captain in basketball or the anchor of the mile relay in track, I secretly craved attention and based my self-worth on playing sports. At the end of high school, I had received some interest from college coaches who wanted me to play varsity basketball or run track, but I ended up only playing club volleyball. At that time, a very quirky dynamic was at work in me though, because I was the one who made decisions that denied myself those other opportunities.

During a city league basketball playoff game following my college days, I was pumped up to play the "enemy." Several of the other team's players were from the team who had beaten my high school team to end our season. The game was going great, until I jumped to block a shot, landed awkwardly and crumpled flat on the floor in pain. I had torn the ACL in my right knee, and, after major reconstructive surgery, the rehabilitation kept me on crutches for six months.

It took me many years to let go of this secret, sport-related self-worth. I finally came to terms with the loss of possible experiences, and the recognition that comes with them, while re-watching *Superman: The Movie*. In the movie, Clark Kent's adoptive father says to him, "There is one thing I do know, son, and that is you are here for a reason. I don't know whose reason, whatever the reason is….But I do know one thing—it's not to score touchdowns." (*Superman: The Movie, 1978*) Yep, that rang true. Finally.

Another major experience that changed my early adult life happened a year after rehabbing from the knee injury. I was on the phone with my sister, discussing our issues with life, and she mentioned I should reach out for help from a counselor. When I said I could handle things on my own, her response changed my life. She said, "That's what Dad would say." *That* was the last thing I wanted to hear, but it got me to take action.

After some procrastination, I finally made the call to a local counseling group. When I met with a counselor, she asked why I was there, so I shared some of my issues of depression and of feeling lost. She asked about my family life as a child, and handed me a brochure about growing up in a home with dysfunction. As I read, I was in shock; it was as if I was reading my life story. The awareness of how my family upbringing affected me woke me up and led me on a journey of self-discovery that continues today.

I eventually left the finance job and found work in the engineering and marketing departments of a lighting company. While there, I read *I Could Do Anything, If I Only Knew What It Was* by Barbara Sher. In the book, Sher talks of helping people find what they really want to do by asking them to describe their "Job from Heaven." They are asked to use their imaginations to think about the hours, activities and environment they'd like best. Many people got enthusiastic thinking about the possibilities, but others were unable to come up with ideas. I, too, had trouble thinking of this type of job. That's when she asked people to picture their "Job from Hell." Now *that* I could describe! My immediate response was, "I'd hate to wear a tie the rest of my working life!" If you can believe it, that internal response is what got me to really begin searching for my passion.

I started to realize that helping people was more of what was on my mind and in my heart, so I volunteered for human resource opportunities at my company: running bowling parties, helping with United Way campaigns, scheduling fitness days, etc. The extra activities met my yearning for a while, but didn't really do the trick. They really couldn't have.

I also had the idea that I wanted to inspire kids, since I had wasted those athletic opportunities by losing myself in college. I wanted to help prevent kids from making the same mistakes that so many of us make at that time of our lives. When I was about twenty-eight, I spoke to a group of high school students about making good choices and about the potential they have. In reality, I was still a lost soul, with little to offer. Although I had been through a few serious life experiences by then, I didn't have nearly enough life experience or "wisdom" to offer any real guidance to students. I hadn't made it through enough of a "victim" mentality or re-found the passion in my life. I needed to live, learn and go through much more before I'd have anything truly useful to say.

Before joining the teaching profession, I spent many years agonizing over what I could do with my life. I took a social work class but didn't get into the program because of a waiting list. I tried pursuing a Master's degree in communication at a local university but contracted chicken pox, followed by a spell of Bell's palsy, which forced me to drop out of the program. I remember my advisor, who was the chair of the department, warned me that dropping out of the program as an older student would make it that much harder to restart the next semester. Later that year, when the fall semester was getting underway, I said to myself, "I'm going to prove that advisor wrong; he doesn't know who he's dealing with!" But sitting in my apartment right before registration started for the semester, I realized the communication class I had taken wasn't really that inspiring. I would be finishing the program just to prove that advisor wrong. I decided right then not to return, and thank God for that decision.

> *"I wish you were 10,000 years old,*
> *because you'd have a really long beard,*
> *you'd be shorter—all shriveled up—*
> *and we could dig up your bones!"*
> Teddi, 4th grader

It's very ironic, but I used to be afraid of children. In my twenties, I didn't know anything about being around them, so I was apprehensive with them. When friends of mine started having kids, I realized how cool they were. Once I spent just a bit of time around them, I realized all they needed was time and attention, and things would grow from there.

People have asked me where I got the idea of getting into teaching. It was not a huge "aha" moment, but rather an idea that built over time, with one experience leading to another. After a few more years of grueling boredom at my corporate job, I began thinking about whether teaching might be an option. I started spending vacation days from my job visiting teacher friends of mine in their classrooms to make sure my "romanticized" thoughts on teaching met with reality. Many did, some did not.

Two of these experiences helped me make the career decision. First, after spending three hours in a fourth grade classroom, several of the students hugged me when I left because I had let them try to jump to reach my very outstretched hand. (At 6'5", my outstretched hand is high to reach for a ten year old!) Those simple hugs made an impression, since I had barely talked with those students. On another occasion, something similar happened. As I walked to my car after visiting a fifth grade classroom at another school, one of the students made a point of yelling "goodbye" to me from across the grass playground. This from a kid I had barely talked to. In just a few minutes, without much communication, there was a certain level of connection. Can you beat that?! These small yet powerful reactions left a mark on me, and I thought, "Wow!"

Then I remembered one moment in a high school calculus class when a classmate asked a question, only to have the teacher re-explain the same concept and not answer the student's question to any satisfaction. The student was still confused, and I knew exactly what he was asking. I remembered thinking to myself, "I could help him; I could teach this." That thought got lost in the deep recesses of my mind for nearly twenty years; it was never brought up to anyone, not even to myself...that is, until I began searching for my real purpose in life. When I had finally searched my soul and entered a teacher certification program, the thought re-surfaced in my conscience as I wrote a reflection for class.

Over the years, my reality and vision of teaching have been altered by years of experience and time with students. There have been opportunities to cry from laughing, to struggle so much it felt like I was having a nervous breakdown, and to feel goose bumps on my arms watching youthful zeal. I've come to learn that teaching is a crazy, mind-numbing, heart-warming, tearful, tough, relentless, fulfilling career. But it was also the best decision of my life. If you want to talk about learning something new every day, teaching is the profession to join. Many days are smooth, with almost lyrical, lovely learning. On other days though, things can be pure chaos and confusion, and I wonder where the day went astray. But then I compose myself and know it was just one day out of many. I remember that the school year must be viewed as a whole instead of judging success on only one day or one lesson.

One of the most frightening times of my career happened during my student teaching. I was teaching with Mark Horowitz, a thirty-year veteran of the profession, and expectations were very high in his classroom, both for his students and for his student-teachers. Honestly, I was intimidated.

During the semester, we split the class for math instruction; I kept about two thirds of the class in the main room and taught the "regular" group, while he took the more advanced students into a back room for their lesson. After teaching my group for several weeks, it became apparent there were at least two levels of students in the group. I thought it would be a good idea to split them into two groups and two lessons, so I mentioned this to Mark. To my surprise, he said, "Go ahead." The only problem was that both sections would have to be taught during the same forty-five minute time frame. Although I knew this before I even mentioned it, my mind and emotions yelled, "What have I gotten myself into?!" I went home, and, being the perfectionist I am, thought I had to figure it out *that night!* I almost had a nervous breakdown. And that's not an exaggeration.

I thought I was losing my mind, from fear. The pressure I put on myself to get it solved that night nearly paralyzed me. I couldn't think straight and was at a loss for how to solve the problem and how to relax. I tried calling two professors to see if they could help, but neither was available. After at least two hours of utter confusion and despair, an idea came to me. Why not split the time up into sections and try to juggle two groups in a way where some students were working on challenge problems while I taught a mini-lesson to others? In theory, it sounded good having two sections alternating between lessons and challenge problems. In application, it didn't quite work out. But it was a start.

The lesson here was to start somewhere, and not put too much pressure on myself to be perfect with everything. My other lesson was that feeling helpless, lost, clueless and scared to death may be part of the job!

One of the words I've used to describe teaching is "relentless." The needs of students are relentless, the need for good lessons is relentless and the pressure to be a professional is relentless. This relentlessness can be both positive and negative— positive because it pushes me to work hard and put everything I've got into my teaching, and negative because that pressure can stress me out or get me too frustrated trying to meet all the needs of students at the same time. But even though relentlessness is part of the job, I wouldn't want it any other way. The relentlessness helps me focus and forces me to create a learning environment that is fresh, dynamic and unpredictable.

During my first four years of teaching, I taught in a fourth to sixth grade Montessori classroom, so there were students at all levels of development. That experience shaped my ability to differentiate subjects and lessons…shoot, I had to! I learned to use my creativity in a variety of ways at the Montessori school. But I wasn't Montessori-trained and after four years there, it was time for a change. I wanted to move out of my hometown, too, to grow personally and professionally.

From there, my experience took me to a downtown Milwaukee urban school, as the Math Teacher Leader and sixth and eighth grade math teacher. I hadn't thought about the level of math that eighth graders learn since I was in junior high school, so I had to relearn things, such as exponential growth, linear equations and inverse relationships. Many teachers seem to fit into this category, teaching math they haven't thought of in years. That can be a scary, insecurity-inducing aspect of teaching.

The first years of teaching are tough and challenging, no matter the preparation, no matter the attitude, no matter the excellence a teacher strives for. I learned things I never expected. Learning in college education classes is one thing, but taking that learning and putting it into practice is a whole other thing. It was at these two schools, the Montessori school and the school in Milwaukee, that I learned how to teach math creatively, without a book, and it has made all the difference in student learning.

After pondering my philosophy and approach to teaching in general, and to teaching math specifically, some themes run through everything I do. I design my classroom to have a lot of heart. My main goals are for students to love learning and to want to come to school because they never know what might happen. The following chapters go into more detail about how heart affects my classroom approach (Mumbo Jumbo: Chapters 1-6), and how math can be taught creatively, without books (Banana Peppers: Chapters 7-12). Although the second half of the book focuses on math instruction, it is filled with ideas that can be applied to all subjects.

I've written this book to relate many strategies to help take teaching and learning to a new level, but I must mention something of utmost importance: connecting with students. Since much of my teaching is based on relationships, the first two chapters discuss the process and thoughts that go into connecting with kids. To get into more detail about the heart I put into teaching, Chapter One talks about what I believe are the basics of building connections with students using heart, trust, expectations, stories and humor. Chapter Two continues the discussion on connection by describing an experience when I dressed up as The Grinch Who Stole Christmas. Chapter Three is all about foundational classroom elements where it's okay not to know something, learning is fun and expectations are high. Chapter Four explains my view of room dynamics and classroom management. In Chapter Five, I share a learning experience and how it shaped my thoughts on being a reflective teacher. Chapter Six is all about working with parents.

The second part of the book focuses on engaging math instruction. Chapter Seven shows how integrating subjects and differentiating learning according to students' abilities is critical in any subject. Chapter Eight begins my explanation of teaching math in a unique way by sharing a special fourth grade box project. Chapter Nine gives examples of how I bring real-world math into the classroom. From there, Chapter Ten goes into extreme detail about how to understand student thinking and use explicit math instruction. In Chapter Eleven, there is a glimpse into how to take student ideas and integrate them into instruction. Chapter Twelve provides many examples of how to make math instruction creative, engaging and relevant.

In reading this book, I truly hope you'll encounter new ideas and, if you are teaching, be moved to take an approach that takes into account your students' thoughts, feelings and desires.

PART I: MUMBO JUMBO

Heartfelt Classroom Teaching

After seeing another student show
signs of needing an appendectomy:
"If Melissa has to get her appendix out,
we ALL need to get ours out!"
Jayson, High Schooler

Chapter 1

Fist Bumps–Connecting with Students

Heart

When I decided to get into teaching, I wanted to do it as much with my heart as with my intellect. While in the certification program, the education I received touched on both aspects, with work on the pedagogy of teaching, lesson planning, and classroom management, plus many reflections on the heart given to teaching. In addition to books on the science of teaching, we also read classic books on the art of teaching, from Herb Kohl and Alfie Kohn to Parker Palmer. These books continued to push me and made me ponder just what kind of teacher I wanted to be.

You may also be getting into teaching because of your heart—you have a calling, want to make a difference, or love to be with children. But how does your heart handle being in the classroom with a bunch of eight-, nine- or ten-year-olds? Is it always great, even for your heart? Do you get heartbroken sometimes? Can it be exhausting and disheartening? These are the kinds of questions that you'll want to be able to answer. And you won't be able to fully answer them until you are actually in a classroom of your own or at least have done some clinical placements.

What do I mean by heart? It's hard to explain and putting words to the concept is like trying to describe love or beauty. By "heart," I mean teaching with concern, a certain priority toward relationships, giving it all you've got and teaching from the greatest part of you. Simply, you care. You could go through the motions, just teach content, learn names, discipline students, grade papers or tests and be a distant teacher. But I'm sure you've heard about students who loved teachers who had that "something" that made their teaching, and the learning, special. Was that "something" just content knowledge to pass on, or some fun lessons? It was probably both of those, plus a lot more. Think back on the teachers you had. Did your favorites have heart? I bet they did, in some form.

The biggest part of teaching is connecting with kids on a level that puts them at ease with whomever they are at the time. And letting them know it's okay to be anxious; it's okay to not know how to do something. In a quote attributed to him, Theodore Roosevelt said, "People don't care what you know, until they know that you care." I can't say I've been 100% successful in connecting with all kids, but I do let them know I care.

Connecting with students happens in many ways. For instance, I like to shake students' hands every morning; it's a good thing to connect with each other and it teaches them to do it properly when they get older. No flimsy, weak handshakes allowed. But I've had to clarify the reason for the handshake.

At the start of one year, I told students that I wanted to share a handshake every morning, but didn't explain the "why" of it sufficiently. I had some students trying to ignore the gesture, which, come to find out, was because of a lack of communication on my part. What I realized was that some of the students thought the handshake was a one-way gesture of respect—that they were supposed to shake my hand out of respect for me. But that wasn't the goal I had in mind at all. My reason was for both of us to show respect for each other: not just them toward me, but me toward them also. I want to shake their hands to let them know that I see them, I am glad they're in class and we can connect again this school day. Once I shared my reasoning in a more explicit way, most students were more forward in their approach to shaking hands, with some even vying for the first handshake of the day.

I also occasionally like to sit with students in the cafeteria for lunch, because it helps me get to know them, and vice versa. I had a teacher once ask me if I was more open to sitting with students because I didn't have kids of my own, implying that if I had my own kids, I wouldn't want to spend so much time with children from my school. When I think about it, if I had my own children, I would still use the same approach to connecting with my students, but would probably be even better at it. As I discussed this approach with a professor friend of mine, he mentioned that when he was a principal, to keep connecting with the students of his school while knowing he needed to also be a dad, he built in time with his family to overlap with his time at school. If there was an ice cream social, he brought his kids to the school. In essence, he figured out a way to keep connecting with students even though he had his own family. That's a great vision to believe in.

"You're such a meany pants!"
Amanda, 4th grader

Amanda spoke these words after I was pretty stern at the end of the school day, trying to get students to be quiet so we could hear the dismissal names being announced. It was one of my more frustrating times of the school day, trying to keep kids quiet as they were excited to leave for the day. So, after raising my voice for the "umpteenth" time, I looked at some students and said light-heartedly, "I know, I'm so mean!" From that came Amanda's response to call me "Meany Pants." And you know what? What's wrong with that? It wasn't disrespectful and it wasn't inappropriate. Once in a while students might push it with a comment, and we talk about boundaries of respect, but having the ability to create something better than an authoritative connection is key to building relationships. Does having nicknames make the learning or discipline in the room any less? No way. In fact, having this light-hearted approach has been my goal.

The beginning of the year doesn't start out this way though. It takes a lot of communicating—discussing and listening to connect. And maybe a little sarcasm too!

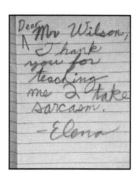

Our first weeks are like most others—setting up expectations and the schedule, doing team-building activities, making sure kids feel the room is theirs, and getting to know each other. These weeks are also used to open up about the learning process and about being real.

"Mr. Wilson, you smell like earth...
in a good way."
Amir, 5th grader

My heart has definitely been touched by teaching and connecting with students, but that doesn't mean I haven't questioned myself or the profession, or that I haven't had insecurities or made mistakes. And I've also had to wake up to the reality of what my role as a teacher really is. Sometimes, I have realized I am just a teacher and not a student's parent or friend. Other times, I have realized, yes, I am more than just another adult in their lives. I can make a huge difference, even though sometimes it feels as if I am just a temporary guide. In reality, that is what I am most of the time. It can be tough to give so much heart to students and then not be able to stay a part of their lives. This has not changed the heart I have for students. And sometimes it depends on the situation. The next story from a year at the Montessori school illustrates a tough realization for me.

The day after the school year ended, there was a Relay for Life cancer walk at a local high school. I had just spent approximately 180 days of the last school year with my students, and we had had pretty good connections. This was the day I realized that for the majority of students, even if there is a close relationship, being their teacher is different than being a member of their family or friends. They may have respected me, liked me, learned from me and even felt close to me. But the day after school ended, and we weren't in a classroom, the students I ran into didn't know what to say to me. They almost acted like we didn't have any relationship. Internally, I said, "C'mon, we spent a whole year in school together that ended yesterday, and now you can barely even say hello?!" It was a weird feeling, very sad in fact. I left the cancer walk feeling very down, realizing I was blessed to have had the opportunity to spend the school year with those kids, but that a special year of school had ended, and with it part of the special connection. Students may remember me and things they learned for a very long time, but life moves on, no matter how bittersweet that was to realize.

Was I going to let that feeling stop me from giving my heart completely to the next class? Not a chance. If you felt that way, would you? I didn't think I'd let a short-term feeling of sadness affect my teaching, but I did learn a boundary that I hadn't thought of before. Knowing that students were in my care for that brief moment of their young lives made me that much more focused and giving. I guess it comes down to setting certain boundaries while still being able to give it all away to your students. It takes a certain strength, courage and vulnerability, which all students may not appreciate, but it will make you a better teacher.

That lesson at the cancer walk happened many years ago, when I was a less experienced teacher. And many things have changed since then—I've learned better strategies, tried new approaches, changed schools, met many students and parents. One thing has not changed and that is my heart for teaching and for students. At my current school, I've been able to see former students on a more consistent basis since they are in my building for lunch and other classes. It has given me a chance to catch up with them, see them grow, give them fist bumps, go to their games, eat lunch with them, see their artwork, and more. I think they understand I care, and want the best for them.

I look forward to seeing my students after they're in my classroom, when they're growing and maturing. And although running into past students whom I haven't seen for some time can be awkward—neither of us knowing quite what to say—it still leaves me glad that I saw them, and they remember the time we spent together. I don't know if they know how much our connections and their growth mean to me. Maybe that's not "professional" enough, to enjoy our time together so much. Maybe it's because I don't have children of my own. Maybe I put too much of myself into our connections, but I don't want to teach another way; I'm still going to continue to make the connections with them. The student outcomes have been too successful for me to change.

I don't put my heart into teaching for the purpose of receiving gratitude or compliments from students, parents, other teachers or administrators. Those are great to receive, but effective teachers just operate this way. They put something into their teaching that is untouchable by compliments, criticism, administration or the future. They know that no matter what they may be feeling or going through personally or professionally, putting their heart into the connections with their students and their learning is the only way to teach.

Student: "*I can't do this math problem.*"
Me: "*Yes, you can, and stop saying, 'I can't.'*"
In her end of year thank you card:
"*Thank you for telling me 'I can.'*"
Ella, 4th grader

Although gratitude is not a reason to put heart into your teaching, some examples of gratitude demonstrate how others appreciate this way of teaching. In my first position as a teacher, we had a rummage sale and silent auction for the tsunami relief effort in 2004. As part of the silent auction, one student's mother, who was a commercial pilot, donated a local flight in her two-person plane. Unbeknownst to me, one family bought it and surprised me the following Monday by saying they had bought it for me. It was the first time I had tears in my eyes from receiving such a kind gesture from a family. I appreciated the gift...and almost lost it during the flight! I've learned keeping my eyes on the horizon is critical and that I'm not too comfortable in small planes—they're too much like roller-coasters, which I can't handle. Another parent told me how much his child liked being in my class, and added that he intentionally waited to tell me while I was standing next to the headmaster of the school. I don't mention these instances to pat myself on the back. I mention them to demonstrate that families appreciate how this type teaching affects their children's lives.

Most adults have a "look" when
they get frustrated with children—
mine is called the "death stare."
It used to work; now it gets chuckles.
"Mr. Wilson, your Death Stare
is really a Hug Stare."
Ethan, 4th grader,
while giving me a hug

At my first school, in a combined classroom of fourth, fifth and sixth grade students, the fourth grade break down was thirteen boys and one girl. Of course, part of my job that year was to keep my eyes on the over-active, fun boys while helping the one girl find and keep her voice. At the end of the year, that young girl brought in a large package and couldn't wait for me to open it. As I removed the tissue paper, a Chicago Cubs logo caught my eye. She knew I was a fan, so she had made me a tied fleece blanket from Cubs logo material. It was one of the most touching times in my teaching career. Knowing the effort she put into making that blanket made my year. There sure is heart in that.

At the end of another school year, I ran into a former student at a local soccer game—she was now going into high school. She and her friends were sitting on bleachers as I walked by, so I waved and said, "Hello." To my appreciation, she left her friends to give me a hug and talk for a while. I even mentioned the funny anecdotes she was involved in that might make this book.

After seeing her, I ran into her parents in a different section of the bleachers. As we talked, they asked if their daughter had left her friends to say "hi." I said she had, and they were impressed that their daughter would leave her friends to talk to me. Do you think she would have done that if I had been a teacher who didn't put heart into my teaching? I doubt it. Heart is where it's at.

> After playfully giving a student a hassle:
> *"You're on thin ice, Mister."*
> Ethan, 4th grader

Trust

Kids need to know we believe in them. I love it when a student tells me, "This is too easy," months after they were saying, "I don't get it" or, "I can't do it." My students learn to trust me enough that, even if they feel confused in the moment, they will "get it." This does not happen by accident. It happens partly because of the way I tell them things will come to them, and about the small steps to getting there, but also because they sense it in the way things operate in the room.

One student's mom, who is also a co-worker, mentioned to me that her son thought I jumped too fast into longer division problems, doing hard problems too soon into the learning process. At first, I didn't think so, but after seeing many errors from many students, I backed off on things. Building trust takes time and the ability to listen, not only to students' comments but to their work. It also means being flexible enough to understand when they have a point in what they're telling me. Do I listen to them? Are their points valid? Do I need to back off, or even give things a breather? Do I even need to apologize for something I did or said in the classroom? How many kids deserve an apology from an adult, but never get one? If it needs to be done, it needs to be done. All of these questions lead me to re-evaluate what I'm doing and adjust from there. Answers to these questions are not signs of weakness or a relinquishing of power, but rather are trust-building events.

Not only do kids learn to trust us, but they may even help us trust them too. Here's an example: an hour after I discussed with students that challenges will occur while growing up, and that my wish for them is that they not give up too easily, I received a lesson of my own. A group of girls from the classroom walked with me out to our school's forest to continue work on a teepee and a wigwam the class was building to sleep in overnight as part of our Native American study. The girls were continuing on with previous progress toward a useable wigwam, with bendable branches connected using wire ties. As I watched them working together, my vision of a livable wigwam started fading. The construction wasn't working very well, and I thought maybe we should just do away with the idea of a good wigwam to sleep in. I tried to sway the girls' thinking toward stopping the wigwam and sticking with just a teepee. They said, "We can do it."

And so they did, with me humbly muttering to myself about how quickly my own confidence had switched off. Thank you, girls, for that awareness.

Learning to trust in each other can happen in any number of ways. Sometimes teachers and students connect while struggling to learn something. At other times, they may connect because of a fun lesson or unexpected events. When the night of the Native American sleepover arrived, we all hoped for good October weather. As it turned out, the wigwam and the teepee were not designed to be totally water-proof. At three o'clock in the morning, the rains came. The girls, sleeping in the teepee, quickly decided that dripping water from the opening at the top was not much fun to sleep through, so they and their chaperones moved into the school building. The boys, sleeping in the rickety wigwam, tried to tough it out, and almost all of them did until morning. When the rains first came, one boy named Joey said he was getting wet while sleeping toward the edge of the wigwam. I offered to walk him inside, but he wanted to stay and just move to the inside of the shelter. About an hour later, Joey declared, "Mr. Wilson, I'm drenched. Can I go inside?" I said, "Put your shoes on, and I'll walk you in." His reply was, "All I have are my slippers." So, I ended up giving him my coat to wear while I gave him a piggyback ride through the pouring rain toward the building. As we scurried down the path, Joey said, "I had a dream I was swimming." He sure was a good sport about the whole situation. You should have seen the inside of the school after we all came into the building at six o'clock that morning. As parents came to pick up their children, wet sleeping bags, mattresses and pillows were strewn about the place.

This sleepover was one more way to build trust within the classroom. We all worked hard to make it happen, and we all went through the night together. It was a great way to become a team within the first two months of the school year. We built camaraderie, and all students shared in the success of the night. And seeing each other with bed-head the next morning sure went a long way in connecting with each other!

Sleepover Aftermath!

Expectations

Another aspect of relating to students is discipline, or what I would rather call expectations and consequences. While I love to connect and have fun with students, everything in a classroom is not fun and games. There has to be some kind of order, structure, and a plan; otherwise, there is chaos. I've learned that while connecting with students, expectations and consequences don't necessarily have to be a negative thing.

When thinking of expectations and consequences, many teachers and students may have a negative paradigm, thinking of scolding or making sure kids are controlled at all costs. I have to admit, there are times when I've thought this myself, or in the heat of frustration want to think that way. But expectations and consequences in a classroom do not have to be negative. Students need, and actually want, classroom expectations and guidance. Even if they initially resist some things, as teachers we have to be strong in our conviction of our plan and let students know the expectations are always high. Are they always reached? No. But having certain high expectations and consequences in the room will provide students with the environment they need. And I make sure to use the term "expectations" with students. It's not just some nebulous idea out there, but a real concept we use in conversation, so that everyone knows what is expected and why. I also let them know there are expectations for me too, which include caring guidance, good instruction, realness, honesty, and flexibility.

My view of consequences versus discipline for students who do not meet expectations has had to change a lot over the years. And I've had to review my own flaws in how I may handle things. Yes, I have high expectations of students, in terms of both behavior and effort. But if I am honest, I don't even meet my expectations of myself, so I've had to learn to get off my high horse. For instance, I've raised my voice more than I ever thought I would, especially early in my career. Kids can be frustrating. Feeling unsure about how to handle a particular situation can be frustrating. One thing I know for sure is that raising my voice every so often will definitely get students' attention, but if it happens too often, it's a terrible thing for a classroom and for students. Because of this, my consequences usually don't include showing my frustration, but rather having a stern conversation, with an understanding heart.

Just yesterday, I had a talk with a student because he was falling behind on some of his work. I also e-mailed his father, just to let him know his son was struggling a bit and that he was a little behind on a project. Later that same afternoon, the father came to the room after school to discuss the concern—we talked about the issues and then he stepped out to ask his son to come into the room to further the discussion. As he came back into the room with his son, I could hear that the son was a bit scared to come in to talk. Right at that moment in my mind and heart, I knew what I needed to tell that student. I told him I was teaching him because I wanted him to be successful, and asked what I could do in this situation to accomplish that. It put him at ease and the three of us figured out a plan. It was a great conversation that happened after months of earlier talks with the entire class, months spent building trust—months that led to this student believing that, even if he felt scared, we could figure things out.

Not to harp on this one boy, but his choices regarding his homework can provide another example of using fair and logical consequences to provide discipline. You see, earlier in the week, one of his classmates asked if students could give *me* homework for a change. I got a kick out of her question, and both for fun and to further my connection with the students, I told them if they wrote two to three great questions in their journal overnight, I would write answers in their journals the next time they were due. If they did this, they wouldn't have homework the next time. They jumped at the chance to have a night off. The next morning, all of the journals were turned in but one, from this same boy. I asked him why he hadn't done his work, and he said he forgot. Guess what? Now he had to spend some time with me at recess writing his two or three questions. Plus, since he hadn't met the criteria for *not* getting homework the next time, he had to do that assignment, too. He got that. There were no arguments and or displays of disappointment. He knew he hadn't met the expectations, which had been clear and weren't very hard to reach, so he accepted the consequence.

Consequences that are natural and based on relationships are better than taking punitive action. My consequences are not hurtful, but come from my desire to see my students learn.

My homework assignments are not meant to stress students, but are meant to help them become successful. We talk about consequences based on expectations all the time in class. I let students choose their seats as long as they are focused and not goofing off. If they don't meet the expectations, they know moving their seat will be a fair consequence. In our morning circle meeting at the beginning of the year, boys were sitting next to boys, girls next to girls. After a few days of verbal reminders to stay focused, I brought up the concern and recommended they sit boy-girl, boy-girl. They didn't even argue the point, because they knew there was a good reason for the new rule and it was fair.

One of my expectations in class is that students give their full effort. I can see missing an assignment once in a while, but I do expect a lot from my students. Often times, when I see poor effort, I assume there is a reason behind it that I must try to understand. At other times, the low effort level is a habit that has to be replaced with a better work ethic. I'll start trying to change a bad habit such as this by having conversations with students about their effort level. If that doesn't work, I try it again. If that doesn't work, a call home may be required. One of the things I bring up in one-on-one conversations, or with the whole class, is that some students "get" things easier than others. Some students have to try really hard to be successful in certain subjects, and see their peers as more proficient. It could be in any subject area: spelling, math, writing or any other aspect of learning.

Students understand this and know they usually fit into one of these groups, depending on the subject. We discuss this, and I tell them that *not* doing their work because they are good at a subject is not only disrespectful to my goals for them, but it is also disrespectful toward their classmates who have to work harder. This way of thinking gets students to take the idea of trying their best to a new level. It's not just work; it has greater meaning in the whole scheme of things. Students show their integrity by using their talents to the best of their abilities. They understand this and know it's a good thing.

An example of students' desire for certain levels of expectations and consequences may help get the idea across a bit more. Before I was a teacher, I volunteered for a Junior Achievement program through a local middle school. I assumed the cooperating teacher would have my back while working with his students, but it ended up that I had to confront some unacceptable behavior myself when some students acted up. One student reacted by being quiet and sucking her thumb, so the relationship I had with this student became a bit fragile. For one session later in the year, I brought in a digital camera and took photos of each student. When I brought copies the next week, this student asked if I could take a few more, so I agreed. On my last day with them a week later, and since her grandmother worked at the same corporation as I did, this same girl asked if she could visit me at the company if she happened to be in the building. Of course, I said yes. I've always felt that this connecting question materialized for three reasons: she was gently asked to be quiet, which was a request she actually respected and needed, I was willing to keep having faith in her, and I went out of my way with the digital photos.

This story is an example of how students need expectations and can respond to gentle discipline. Secretly, students really want some sort of structure and discipline in their lives, both of which they may not have in their homes lives. Most students will respect a structured environment and the consistency of discipline with fair consequences, especially if given with gentle redirection for learning purposes. I make a point of using the term "expectations" with students all the time. It gently gives them a reason why certain behaviors are requested. By using "expectations" they can see that it is a goal to reach, because in the long run, it helps improve their learning. I think kids get that.

Stories

Sharing stories is a very warm way to connect and share ideas that may not be in the "normal" school curriculum, but may be just as important. I share many experiences with students. I never try to sway students one way or another politically or religiously, or tell them too much about family or relationship issues. But that doesn't mean I cannot share stories from my own life. They love to tell their own stories and also like to hear them from others.

This sharing of stories builds trust by showing how human we all are; most of us can relate to stories in one way or another. Stories open up new avenues for learning, connecting and sharing heart in a classroom. Some stories tug at our hearts, while others may be more lighthearted. Both bring people closer together.

Here's a story I like to share that shows that their teacher can make mistakes. While volunteering for a youth church group, I was asked to run the activities after the mid-week service, which would include things like setting up volleyball and basketball courts in a multi-purpose room. No big deal, right? Well, that was until the leaders of the program thought it would be cool to introduce my assistant and me to the two hundred or so middle and high school students in a special way.

On the first night of the program they decided to introduce us as if we were professional basketball players, with a hoop and strobe lights setup in front of the students, and us running in to dunk a ball in front the crowd. It was planned well and would have worked out perfectly if I hadn't decided to try a 360-degree jump before dunking. You see, I used to be able to do that kind of dunk on a rim at a normal height of ten feet, and this rim was only going to be set at nine feet—it should be a piece of cake, I thought. Except that I couldn't quite jump like I had in the past—not even close. But of course, in my mind, I could still pull it off.

When the time came, I dribbled a ball down the middle of crowd, tried to jump, and left the ground by about two inches. Yes, my show-off dunk got blocked by the rim and led to a twisted ankle and bruised back from falling on the stage next to the basketball hoop. My much younger assistant then jumped over me as I lay on the ground. After that, I had to get up and introduce myself and the activities I had planned to the shocked crowd. You would have thought they all would have been laughing, but they couldn't quite figure out what they had just seen! This is a story I like to tell to students because it makes their teacher human. And it shows them it's okay to make mistakes. As I left the church that evening, another volunteer mentioned to me, "I know you felt a bit embarrassed by the fall, but you know, more kids can relate to you because you fell than if you would have finished the dunk." How right she was.

> *"Why do we use the words*
> *MEDIUM and MEDIAN?"*
> Peter, 4th grader

To get students to understand that "median" means middle, I've related a story about a group of church friends and me dodging death when a car in front of us tried to pull a U-turn on a Colorado freeway, thus making me swerve into the *median* of the interstate. After discussing the multiple meanings of median,

I ask students to mention, "That is a median," to their parents as they drive down the road. It's a way to get students to connect.

Stories come in all shapes and sizes. That's because we all have a variety of experiences that others can relate to. One such story happens to also be very gross, which of course, students love to hear. It involves high school students at an outfitter in the Boundary Waters of northern Minnesota. In the middle of the night, a commotion in the boys' A-frame cabin startled all of us awake, except for one student. A student had vomited on a top bunk, and as he tried to clean it up, the sleeping student below him woke up, saying, "There's something dripping on me." Now *that* gets a student response! And it gets engagement.

Other stories I share include one about a crazy Boundary Waters storm that hit July 4, 1999, a day after the vomit incident. There's also one about a Jeep accident when I was a junior in high school, one about observing the struggle to find drinkable water while in a third world country, and how things were when I was younger. I also share my recovery from the torn ACL, Bell's Palsy, and a herniated disk in my back, and even the time my miniature wiener dog got sprayed by a skunk. Stories aren't just for fun, but also have many life lessons within them. Very often while I tell a story, students raise their hands to share their connection to the story. Internally, I say "Yes!" when students connect and want to share their stories too. All of these stories open up worlds of discussions in the classroom, and students are always eager to relate their own stories.

The latest story I've told happened on an April Fool's Day. A few years back, during my third year in teaching, four fourth-grade girls were already in my classroom when I arrived one morning. They were in sleeping bags acting like they had slept there all night. (One girl's mom was a colleague of mine at the school). As I walked in, I could hear them giggling, so I knew something was up. A second later, they all jumped out of their bags and shot Silly String at me, which was very fun. After a few seconds, they stopped and we all laughed, and they started cleaning up. But they didn't know this wasn't the end of it. Thinking fast on my feet, I grabbed one of the cans of Silly String as they cleaned up and hid it for later. At the end of the day, as all the other students watched from the hallway, I asked the four of them to come and see me; I had something to talk to them about. That's when I got them back and sprayed them with the string! Now *that* was fun. That was a connecting moment.

> *"I don't tell jokes to be funny or*
> *to be the center of attention—*
> *it's to build relationships and*
> *to deepen the learning."*
> Dr. Peter Jonas (Jonas, 2014)

Humor

Some of the other fun, wise-guy things I've done really get kids to feel special, or at least acknowledged. Whether it's been sneaking up on Ezekiel every day at lunch to put my fist down on his plastic bag of marshmallows (which of course just bounce back to their original shape), putting an unsolvable problem on the April 1st daily mini-math, giving Eily a "ticket" for eating her dessert before her lunch, giving kids the "death stare" for goofing off too much, or saying, "Eat your crust!" to kids in lunchroom to get on their case, they know a teacher can be lighthearted and still be very caring, with high expectations. I am definitely not the only teacher doing this type of thing—all kinds of teachers connect with students this way. They find a way to that is natural to them and build on their own strengths.

Here's one last story from my first year of teaching that I *don't* tell students, but it sure was a funny incident. Growing up in the 1960s and '70s, flip-flops were sometimes called thongs. During that first year of teaching, I had students share information about trips they went on. They would stand in front of a map, point to where they had gone, and tell us a bit about their trip. The plan was to get more geography into the classroom, and also let students share part of their lives. On this occasion, a fourth grade student named Sam began talking about his trip somewhere warm with a beach. As he talked about his feet getting hot on the sand, I asked, "Sam, why didn't you wear some thongs?" As the words left my mouth, it hit me that thongs nowadays aren't the same as thongs were when I was growing up! Yes, that was the first real LOL moment of my career as students cracked up and I got embarrassed. That was a funny moment I will never forget. Later in the year, three students from class found an American Greetings card that showed two older women walking down the beach. As they handed me the card, they said, "We *had* to get this for you!" Connecting with students can take many forms!

Reproduced by Permission.
American Greetings Corporation
©AGC, LLC

We've had many laughs together, but humor and stories also help us bring heart into the classroom, because we end up talking about real issues. And I also get to answer meaningful life questions that might not ever come to light except through stories.

There are many ways to connect with students. My choices include using my heart, building trust, communicating expectations and sharing stories and jokes, but there are others. Whatever we choose, we should try to connect with students on a level that makes the learning environment open, warm and fun. We could all use more of that type environment in our everyday lives.

Chapter 2

The Grinch

"The Santa suit smells like rotten eggs."
Maddie and Hanna Rose,
4th graders

"It should! The Grinch stinks!"
Elena, 4th grader

Connecting with students has come in ways I would never have predicted. Being on stage dressed as a favorite character is one of those unexpected occurrences. As I sat behind the curtain in my latest costume, I was excited, a bit nervous, and very grateful. Since my stage appearances were spaced out during the children's choir performance, it gave me time to meditate about changes in my life and how unrecognizable my life was compared to the depressed corporate worker I used to be. I was so grateful sitting there, listening to elementary students, many now calling me "Mr. Grinch" in the hallways. Just ten or so years ago, I never would have dreamed that I'd be enjoying getting my face painted green and listening to young students singing for their parents. And what a hoot it's been to be able to come out of my teacher character to be creative and goofy, while at the same time connecting with my students.

Several years before I was teacher, my very good friend, Tally, called to ask me a question. She sat on the parent association of the school her three children attended, and its members were asked if they knew someone tall and thin who could dress up as the Cat in the Hat. I can just imagine the smirk that came across Tally's face. She called me within minutes to hint that I had been volunteered! Dressing up for that school and those students gave me my first glimpse into connecting with students in unusual ways.

After becoming a teacher, the first character I was asked to play was the Statue of Liberty. The sixth grade students in my Montessori classroom were given the assignment of creating a skit around the subject of the mass immigration to the United States in the early 1900s. After a day of brainstorming, they asked, "Can we make it a musical, and will you be the Statue of Liberty?" Of course, I had to say yes. They found me a foam crown and a fake torch, and I found a drab green sheet to wear around myself like a toga. During the skit, they stopped their performance as the Statue of Liberty joined them on stage. They then asked the audience to stand and join them as we all sang the *Star Spangled Banner*. Now that was fun!

"You're not mean, you're green."
Sara, K4 Student

These chances to dress up and become a different character prepared me slightly for my biggest and most enjoyable role. Last autumn, my school's music teacher approached me to ask if I would play the *Grinch Who Stole Christmas* in the annual holiday concert. I didn't hesitate to say yes.

For the show, I was scheduled to be on stage three times: in the opening number of first through fourth graders singing "You're a Mean One," as a Santa stuck in the chimney in a call and response song with first and second graders, and finally with fourth graders reading a short story of how the Grinch has his heart grow, with our youngest, three-year-old students hugging me.

As the date of the concert approached, I was told four high school students had volunteered to help me transform into the Grinch. Backstage before the concert, these students used three-inch wide brushes to paint green makeup onto my face, ears, neck, arms, hands and even nostrils. Yes, it took weeks to remove the paint from my inner ears!

After the paint dried, powder was applied to prevent the paint from rubbing off. Lydia, a senior, did most of the powder application, along with her younger sister Hannah. As I sat there, I thought how weird it might be doing this to a teacher. But kids are so great, it's just something they chose to do. As they applied the powder, I faintly smelled onions, but didn't say anything until Lydia later said, "If my hands smell like onions, it's because I just had a submarine sandwich for dinner." That is honesty.

Lydia and Hannah powdered my hands, arms, neck and ears before starting on my face. As Lydia began on my face, she realized the best way to apply the powder would be to blow it off a small pillow onto my face. So, she went ahead and blew powder onto my face. I said to her, "I bet this is the last thing you thought you'd be doing your senior year!" Although to these makeup appliers it might have been an interesting and curious thing to do during their school year, to me it was another way to connect to previously unknown students.

During rehearsals, no students had seen me with the green makeup applied. Before the real deal though, I snuck into the music room behind the stage, in full makeup and Santa suit, to say hi to all the anxious first through fourth graders preparing to enter the stage to start the concert. It was good to let them see me in my getup before they saw me on stage; it probably reduced any laughter they might have had. But since our youngest students were in a different room, I had no chance to see them while in my green makeup. The first time they saw me in my green face paint was when they first encountered me on stage.

My first two appearances on stage went as planned, but as I entered the stage for the last time, which was the appearance with the youngest students, a little part of me became worried. While I acted out my part, I watched as these sweet students reacted to seeing me. Most of them continued doing their parts after hesitating just a split second, but one young girl backed away from me, trying to grasp in her innocent mind what was going on, and if she should trust me. She hung on for a while, but then scurried off stage, not totally scared, but not totally okay with me either. As the other students completed their parts, and the fourth graders read the story, I returned to be met by a hug and "Merry Christmas, Mr. Grinch" from a third grade Cindy Lou Who. I then acted like my heart grew three times as big and the young students all hugged me as I bent down on one knee. Even the little girl who had left the stage came out to give me a hug. It wasn't planned, but it sure was "just right" for everyone involved to see her come out to hug me after being a bit out of sorts. That must have been serendipity at work.

After the concert, many students wanted their picture taken with the Grinch, and I ended up driving home still in character: painted green, wearing a Santa suit, and giving other drivers the Grinch scowl. That was a good way to end a great teacher night.

When I volunteered to play the part of the Grinch, I didn't think of the ramifications it would have. I didn't expect that students would want to call me "Mr. Grinch" when they saw me in the hallways, although now that it's happened, I should have seen that coming. I didn't expect to connect with students in other ways, either. When you get stopped in the lunch line by a teacher of three-year-olds and get asked to make a special appearance for her students, it's pretty special. They wanted to meet the Grinch in person, not just get to say hello in the hallway. It was a special moment to give them the Grinch scowl and make their day. In one instance, the Grinch was even considered better than Tylenol! That's what I heard from our school secretary as she tended to an ill student who got a kick out of the Grinch stopping in to give her a scowl.

This kind of commitment to getting outside of my shell to connect with students goes well beyond the classroom. Very young students who were scared to even look at me because I was so intimidating now stop in the hallway to connect with me as I give them Grinch scowls—all because I painted my face green. Those same young students will be in my classroom in a few years. And although I may have looked a bit foolish acting the part, this kind of action lets children know teachers can be vulnerable to trying something new, thereby modeling the kind of willingness to try that I hope they learn. I hope to model a willingness to go after an unknown out of curiosity and adventure, rather than a hesitancy to try something new out of a fear of looking silly or "failing."

Even parents have seen the power in my becoming the Grinch. Two weeks after the performance, after a lower school assembly, a parent of a third grade student approached me while we put chairs away and said, "I think I see some green paint behind your ears!" He went on to say how special it was to watch. I had never talked with this parent before, and now we were talking Grinch and green paint, and about how it became a way to connect with kids. He got it.

There was also one final perk. I was able to give scowls to people for weeks, before and after the concert. You can't beat that freedom, especially when morning scowls are the usual for this non-morning person!

> *"Mr. Wilson, can you help me*
> *sharpen this green pencil?"*
> Audrey, 5th grade student

> *"Sharpen it with your Grinch teeth!"*
> Olivia, 5th grade student

Chapter 3

Foundational Classroom Elements

While I was watching students roller skate:
Student: *"Mr. Wilson, how come you're not skating?"*
Me: *"Well, I have bad knees and a bad back."*
Student: *"Mr. Wilson, you skate with your feet!"*
Olivia, 3rd grader

The first two chapters discussed connecting with students in ways that make them comfortable and make me available to them. It's one thing to connect with students, but what about the learning that is the ultimate goal? The next chapters go into detail about how great learning can be an extension of interpersonal connections.

Kids want to learn and work hard. Sometimes there are challenges, but the love of learning is there—it can just get squashed by many things: insecurities, meaningless lessons, bad teaching or intimidating teachers, useless rules, tough home circumstances, ill-advised messages from parents, forced compliance and much more.

I've seen kids get forced to memorize specific definitions of words, word for word, instead of in words that reflect their own understanding. This requirement comes from rules made to get students more in line with a teacher's goals for their obedience rather than for their learning. I've also seen parents tell their kids that what is taught in schools is useless. I've seen teachers get frustrated with students, and I've done enough of that myself. Do these examples keep students motivated to keep learning and trying? Most likely not. That's why I continue to grow as a teacher myself.

So, what will help keep kids motivated and excited about learning? In education schools, future teachers learn about learning styles and intelligences, but how do teachers take the theories and get them into practice? Most teachers have great intentions of creating awesome lessons and a warm learning environment. But even with great intentions, the reality of time and stress set in, making many goals of awesome learning turn into plain, old-fashioned, boring lessons and days. Relationships can also get tarnished when frustration sets in.

Conversations

The start of a school year gives teachers the chance to awaken their students' spirits to a great year of learning and growing. In my classroom, we start out by discussing certain ideas and by interacting in fun, challenging ways. One concept we talk about is homework.

I explain that my main job is *not* to give them homework, but to *help them to learn*. It's that simple, and my honest explanation sets up students to see the goals of my lessons and homework from a whole different perspective. Many students find this refreshing and some actually cheer. I explain to them that it's not my job to make them stressed out, or force them do work night after night. My job is to help them to learn as much as they can while I have them as students. Sometimes that involves homework, sometimes it doesn't.

> While eating lunch together,
> *"I love when we have these little conversations*
> *with teachers, because they're so intriguing."*
> Mason, 3rd grader

To motivate students and also to show I care about each student's learning, I must have frank, honest, friendly conversations with them. But these take time and effort to grow and nourish. Most of the time, I connect with students rather quickly, but it's not always instantaneous. I have to go out of my way to form a connection, whether it's joking with them, or eating lunch with them. Some students and I just don't seem to click, but that doesn't mean I don't try. Most students are open to the conversations.

In one instance early in the school year, my co-teacher and I noticed a fourth grade girl not paying enough attention to lessons. I called her over and asked if she was paying enough attention in class. Her answer was very honest, saying flat out, "No." I chuckled because it was nice to hear pure honesty.

She told me she couldn't see the board very well, plus her chair was angled in a bad way at a round table, making her sight line even more difficult. We came up with a simple solution—move her to a more appropriate seat. It's a simple example, but she was honest because she trusted she could be. That trust was developed by cultivating a relationship, letting her know that I cared, that I would listen and that her learning was my objective.

This instance is also a good example of why I cannot always assume I know what's going on with everything in the room. As a teacher, there's something about being in control that is comforting. And part of that control, in an unhealthy way, could be that we think we know everything and must be in total command of things, out of insecurity. I could have easily thought that student wasn't paying attention because of an attitude, rather than some logical explanation. By the end of the year, this young girl was a sponge for learning and was asking for more and more challenge.

One other aspect of communication with students that I learned the hard way was that I don't always need to have the last word in a conversation. In one of my early classrooms, a student handled himself very well most of the year, but occasionally would lose it and explode for unknown reasons. Even his mother didn't know why or when the outbursts would occur. Being a newer teacher, I would try to take control of the situation and unfortunately usually made the problem worse than it had to be.

I thought I had to have the last word on settling things down, and keeping this student from disrupting the class too much. Even though I knew maintaining a heated discussion with a student wasn't going to help the situation, the circumstance got to me. On one of these occasions (it happened about three or four times in two years with this student), I realized my reaction was inappropriate. For some reason, I was always trying to get the last word in, thinking I had to show that student and the rest of the class who was in charge.

What I realized was that if I just said my expectations and let him blow off some steam, even having the last word in his frustration, the situation could improve. This is another example of a growing pain for a newer teacher.

Security in *not* knowing, and the learning process

After making a mistake in my corporate job,
and owning up to it with my boss:
"Only the dead don't make mistakes."
Don Wandler, my former boss

As students come into class every year, their thoughts and feelings may turn to being nervous, not knowing how things are going to operate in a new classroom, how they will fit in, whom they will befriend, will they be successful, or will they be supported or bullied. They have a whole lot of guts, even if they don't see it. With all these possible thoughts and feelings going through students, our job is to not deter their spirit, but engage it and help them become the people they were meant to be. I write this because sometimes teachers have high aspirations for their students, but then set up the year making their students feel insecure, and lose some of their courage. Examples from my sister and other friends might best demonstrate this concern.

There are students who love math and are amazing little calculators and problem-solvers, even at a young age. They seem to have an innate math ability. The majority of the time these students are secure about their abilities—I was fortunate to be one of those kids. But many students don't have that obvious ability, although they may have a hidden ability that just hasn't been nurtured, encouraged or challenged enough. A misguided elementary teacher once told my sister her math ability was poor, instead of letting her know she could improve. Another friend had a teacher who handed back math tests from best to worst, and since she was given back her tests last, everyone in class knew she had done badly. They are both now over 50 years old and still remember the experiences; those instances affected their self-confidence in using math for the rest of their lives. These comments aren't just related to math. A co-teacher of mine shared a story of a teacher who told her as a kid that she couldn't carry a tune. She never got over it and doesn't like to sing because of this remembrance from so long ago.

All three of these women grew up thinking they weren't good at something. Those thoughts came from one moment in their lives when an elementary teacher told them that they weren't good at a subject. Think about what those young girls were telling themselves internally that year in their lives. And then think about what kind of year we want our students to have in our classrooms. Words, facial expressions, body language and routines can make a big difference to students. To be honest, I've had my moments thinking or reacting in a way that wasn't as positive or optimistic as it should have been. I care about each student, but frustrations have gotten to me at times, too— I've had to work at improving myself in this regard.

At the start of a school year, I make sure to let students know it is okay to *not* know something. In fact, I try to model some things that I continue to work on or am currently not good at, like playing an instrument or acting. I might even share some of my own insecurities about certain things. This makes me human and shows them it is okay to struggle with things. Kids that might struggle in math or may be "average" sometimes think they should already know lots of things that they really aren't required to at that moment in their lives. They sometimes have these unrealistic notions that others don't have the same insecurities. I explicitly let these students know that *not knowing* is part of learning, and I want to help them bust through their illusions that they can't be good at things.

But how do I do this? By being open about it and being real about it. Students need to see the conviction that I am *not* going to let them fail or struggle beyond their capabilities. I work to get students to trust that I will be there for them, and that they can trust me to lift them up, even if they say things like "I can't" or "I don't get it."

There are plenty of times when I have had to say, "Don't worry, you will get it. I'll help you. Trust me." I tell kids they're going to have to trust that I will help them learn. I tell them they will learn, because I believe in them, and I believe in my own ability to help them. I do not let them see any insecurity in my belief about them, because I *know* it to be true. Kids love this! They need someone who will believe in them even beyond what is visible or imaginable to themselves.

In class, we talk a lot about not knowing things. If students knew everything, why would I need to teach them? It's pretty obvious, but many students need to keep hearing that it's okay to fail and try again. It's okay not to be great at something. Progress is the goal. My goal here is to set students up for success, no matter how small. Some students who are high achievers might not need to hear this as much because they are so successful, but even for them it can't hurt. For others who struggle in different subjects, it gives them a break. It lessens the pressure they may feel, from me, their parents, other teachers, other students, their siblings or even themselves.

My first day schedule always includes a time to talk about not knowing. We talk about the learning process and what it may feel like. I use this drawing to graphically model the process. Most kids have never seen learning put this way.

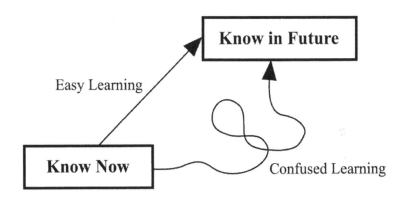

Before explaining the drawing, I ask students what they think it represents. I ask students if they've ever learned something that came easily to them. Most will raise their hands for something like kicking a soccer ball. I explain that this "easy learning" is the straight line from the bottom "Know Now" box to the top "Know in Future" box. "Straight line" learning is fun, exciting and encouraging. Students would like learning more if it was always like that. Too bad that's not always the case.

Students are then asked if they've ever had a tough time learning something, and I add an example from my life. Most kids will again raise their hands, mentioning all kinds of things. I draw a crazy, mixed up, roundabout line between the boxes, and ask them what they think the curved lines means. Many answers are offered.

I then explain to them that the new line is also learning, but it involves confusion. And that is okay. In all honesty, lots of learning is confusing, chaotic, and senseless until somehow an "aha" moment breaks through the nervousness and confusion, for a moment of clarity. I ask students if they've ever felt like they've been "in the confusion" in class. Most will jump to tell you they've been confused while learning something. I make sure they know this is natural and happens to everyone. I don't gloss over this, but explicitly tell them that confusion is okay. A discussion about confusion sets up students to being open to that part of the learning process, or at least it introduces them to the concept. When challenge and confusion come, and they will, I reiterate the concept of learning with confusion being okay. I explain this over and over again. After a while, students begin to trust in my realistic view of learning.

I've seen it happen again and again. Here's an example: initially, many fourth grade students struggle with the standard algorithm for multi-digit multiplication. Months later, after the majority become experts and they start asking for more challenge, I bring them back to months before when it was a challenge. I build them up confidently and with conviction to let them see just how far they've come, without paying much attention to it. All of a sudden they realize they have grown through the confusion. That's when I tell them, "I told you so!" And I once again let them know that if they trust me and the process, and trust in their own ability to learn and get through tough, confusing times, they will learn a lot more than they thought they ever could.

This past spring, as I was teaching several advanced fourth graders basic algebra ($5n + 6 = 31$), it was obvious that one student was in some "crazy confusion." She was asking extra questions, had a flustered face and was becoming frustrated. After a few minutes, we postponed the lesson for a minute and brought up the *Knowing* illustration again—I asked if she thought she was "in the confusion." She agreed, so I encouraged her to trust the process. She did trust, and got through it. Having the ongoing discussion about what it takes to learn helped her work through the confusion to reach success. As a teacher, seeing students make these kinds of breakthroughs is one of the thrills of my job.

The Gong

"Mr. Wilson, what you were saying
was just a bunch of mumbo jumbo,
but now I finally get it!"
Cooper, 4th grader,
hitting the gong

We've all had our "aha" moments—the moment we understand something. It's a good feeling to *finally* know what everyone else seems to have gotten long ago. We're finally in on the joke or knowledge. In my classroom, we make this an event, because it is something to be cherished and cheered. Think about how many students in a classroom might be sitting there wishing they knew what was going on, but are too scared or worried about what others think to raise their hands. The gong I keep in my classroom is a symbol for the celebration of learning. It is also a symbol that says it's okay to not know something beforehand.

Here's the scene: during the middle of a lesson, a student quietly gets out of her seat and slowly makes her way to a small gong, picks up a wooden mallet, and hits the gong. The other students become silent, waiting. The use of the gong is another part of my strategy to make not knowing something okay, and nothing to be ashamed of. It's a way to celebrate learning something new, not hide it—and to help other students who might be struggling with the same questions. When a student hits the gong, I stop talking and the class stops whatever they are doing. After hitting the gong, students must explain why they're up. They can't just say, "I got it," but have to explain what they "got." The whole class claps for them and shows an appreciation for learning, a congratulatory acknowledgment to students.

Since it's such a new concept at the beginning of the year, most students start out being reluctant to hit the gong. But after it becomes part of the class and the learning environment, it's a good event. Celebrating learning is not just a classroom event though. The gong hit for "aha" moments has also moved beyond the classroom to hallways or while outside the school. Now, students sometimes raise their hands to hit the other one symbolically as they walk down the hallway, and other students have even done the same thing at home with their parents.

> **After a multi-gong-hit lesson,**
> ***"I'm feeling 'gongy' all over!"***
> **Elena, 4th grader**

When I first brought the gong into a school, I was visiting a third grade classroom as the math teacher leader and mentioned the gong mallet in my pocket. Sarcastically (and they knew it), I mentioned to the kids that if they didn't behave correctly, I'd give them a light tap on the head with the mallet. Of course, every kid in the class jumped up to raise their hands and yelled "Can you tap me on the head?!" From that moment on, every time I saw some of those students in the hallway, they'd ask to get playfully tapped on their heads. It got to the point where I had to walk around the school with the mallet in my pocket, just to be ready to give them a head tap. But I also told them not to go home and tell their parents Mr. Wilson had hit them on the head!

Although this story is fun, the gong is serious business. Think about how students feel after hitting the gong and receiving acknowledgment of their learning, compared to how they might feel receiving a test that shows them what they don't know. A great classroom should have an environment that is conducive to learning and feelings of being supported. The gong gives students the opportunity to be fully real about their growth and provides them a positive moment in the middle of the day. This positive experience can go a long way in improving students' self-confidence in the learning process, both long-term and in the short run.

Why do we need to learn this?

This is an age-old question every student has thought at one time or another. There are plenty of things that students learn when they're younger that, to their young minds, might not seem to have a real purpose. As a teacher, will you have any good answers for this question? I found a good answer which I use in math, but it can transfer to any subject. It comes from my desire for my students to be successful, knowledgeable, skilled adults. I think they know I mean it and that I want the best for them.

In an article about presidential approval ratings after 100 days in office, the author compared President Obama to Presidents Clinton, Bush, Nixon and others, using statistics presented in various forms to make the article more interesting. There were percentages, decimal numbers, fractions and ratios, such as 63%, .65, $^6/_{10}$ and 6 out of 10. When students ask why they have to learn something, I use this article as an example of why I want them to learn math that might not seem important to them in that moment.

My suggestion to students is that there are probably plenty of adults who cannot understand the comparison between the different ways of representing the data, and end up having to skip that part of the article. And by skipping that part of the article, or stopping their reading because of their lack of understanding, they have missed out on something. I tell students I don't want them to be that kind of adult. Why would I want them to be an adult who has to skip things because they don't understand what it means? Students get that; they get that their teacher is there to help them be successful adults. After that explanation, I have rarely had a student question why they have to learn something.

While discussing math, I also tell students no one has ever come up to me in a store and asked, "Can you change a fraction to a decimal?" or "What is ¾ as a percentage?" No, that is not why we learn math. We learn math as a tool to help us work with and understand the world. When they're adults, students may not need to know exactly how to change a fraction to a decimal number, but if they have an understanding of the relationship, then they will have a better idea of how things work and what they mean. This makes sense to students, too.

Is that a question or a statement?

I encourage my students to be confident problem solvers who are sure in their abilities. At the beginning of the school year, sometimes students give hesitant answers to questions presented in class. This hesitancy in their voices is accepted at the beginning of the year because many ideas and concepts are very new. As the year progresses things start to change—students become more confident and capable, and I become more of a stickler on things. One thing I pick up on is if they're answering questions with the inflection of a question or as a statement. Here's an example. I might ask, "What is five times four?" and students answer with an inflection of a question in their voices: "Twenty?" I stop them in their tracks and ask, "Are you asking me, or are you telling me the answer?" Sometimes they say it really is a question because they aren't sure of themselves. And that's okay. But I also stress that if they know what they are doing, there's no need to phrase answers with a questioning inflection. As they become more confident, they start making stronger statements of their answers.

Zoom

Although learning involves spending lots of time not knowing, there are plenty of ways to make it fun and intriguing. Here is one example of how I bring intrigue into a social studies lesson. On the first day of school, I use *Zoom* by Istvan Banyai to give students a fresh look at the world. In the book, different illustrations are used to give readers a new perspective from page to page, as the view is zoomed out, leading to surprises. We use the softcover book and tear the pages apart from the binding.

To start, students are shown three pages from the back of the book so they can see how the "zooming out" of the book works. I then show them the first page of the book. After this, I divide the students into small groups of four or five. I give each student one page, and I tell them not to let others in their group see their page. Then I allow them to speak to each other about the illustration they have as they try to get themselves in the correct order of zooming out. Other groups of students do the same with other sections of the book. We then come together and slowly place the illustrations, one at a time, on the floor. This lets students see just how much things can change. I tell them this example of changing perceptions can be related to how we look at social studies, such as zooming in on local topics and then zooming out to look at things from a national perspective.

In addition to this, students are each allowed to take one photograph within our classroom using a digital camera. They can zoom in or out on anything within the room, but they can only take one photograph. After all the photos are taken, they are projected onto our Smartboard, showing them how even a classroom can be seen from different perspectives. This leads to a discussion on seeing different details of a topic—that subjects like social studies can be seen from the view of history, culture, economics, or geography.

The drawings below, made the night after the "zoom" activity, demonstrate that students do think about the discussion.

Drawn by Ella B.

This exercise in seeing things from different perspectives, and realizing that things may not always be what they seem, is a good way to get students to understand that we all interpret the world in our own way. Sometimes those interpretations are similar to ours, while often times they are different. This awareness gives students the opportunity to be okay with who they are and the way they think. It also gives them the chance to recognize others' perspectives. As the school year progresses, when ideas or concerns are bought up in class, whether they are similar or different from their own, it's that much easier for students to appreciate and accept another way to look at things. This different perspective often appears in math class, but happens in all areas of learning. Then, instead of reacting to a classmate's idea with a condescending look or comment, students can respect it. This respect often leads to improved learning for more than just one student.

Meadow Music

My first classroom in the Montessori school was called the Meadow. As the year progressed, I started to bring in music with positive lyrics, such as REM's *Shiny, Happy People* or The Beatles' *Here Comes the Sun* and it became known as Meadow Music. I bring music into the classroom for several reasons: to motivate those student who have a musical intelligence, to read lyrics as a language arts lesson, to inspire students with lyrics of kindness and integrity, and to just enjoy the music. It's also a good way to bring in different types of music that cross many generations. Sometimes, students may not get the reasons, and may want to be silly just a bit, but in the long run, the messages sink in and they understand the heart involved as we enjoy the music together.

But I'm not the only one bringing in the music; students start asking to bring in their own, too. As long as lyrics are tame and have a good message, most student choices are approved. Students' ideas have included songs such as *Heart and Soul* by the band Built by Titan, *Happy* by Pharrell Williams or *Forgiveness* by TobyMac. After listening to songs, we have discussions on their meaning. These discussions often bring out differing perspectives or the need to clarify what the lyrics meant. Songs that talk about the *light within* have been explained so that students understand the meaning of goodness that we all have within us. This is one more way for students to connect with what's going on in the room, and also connect with others along the way.

NLA

> After a year of me telling students, "NLA,"
> students were telling me, "NLA."
> *"It's like the apprentices have turned on their master."*
> Will, 4th grader

Students in my classroom learn quickly that NLA means "No Lollygagging Allowed." When we build shelters in the forest for our study of Native Americans, students line up to carry items that we need, and of course, some students at the end of the line always seem to be too far behind. The NLA acronym comes from my high school basketball coach, Coach Belden, who hollered at anyone who was being lazy to quit lollygagging. I share this story with my class, and now, when students hear "NLA," they know to get going.

"NLA" is used throughout the year to make sure kids keep up with the rest of the class, whether it is while transitioning from classroom to classroom, or building to building on the school campus. It becomes an easy, lighthearted way to communicate that students need to keep up. They even use it on me if they run ahead on the sidewalk leading to the school entrance.

30-Second Speeches

"Can we do it again tomorrow?" That's what I hear after the first day I introduce this activity. Think about this quickly—do you like to give speeches? If your heart rate went up, I get it. The majority of people react that way when they think about public speaking. And that is really a shame. We *all* have something to say. That's the way I want my students to view it— I want them to be ready and willing to say what they have to say. This is just one more example of how high expectations are evident in class.

> *"Mr. Wilson, do you think kids can be*
> *quiet and happy at the same time?!"*
> **Will S., 4th grader**

How many times do teachers or other adults ask children to be quiet or just listen? We do it all of the time. And yes, we do need to have some peace and quiet sometimes. But my vision for students is for them to be confident and composed when they share what they know. Because of this, my fourth grade students start giving speeches rather early in the school year. They start with thirty-second speeches and I gradually increase the time frame from there.

For the thirty-second speeches, we discuss things that students probably already know, like how to play hopscotch, how to make a taco or a peanut butter and jelly sandwich, or how to build a snowman. The ideas are all thrown in a bucket and students are called one at a time to pick their topic. If they know the topic, they must stick with it; if they really don't know enough about the topic, they can pick again. Once all students have their topics, I allow them ten to fifteen minutes to think about what they want to say and to make props. The classroom becomes a picture of movement and excited energy. But, they are focused.

I ask for volunteers to be the first speakers, and I write the order of speeches on the board. When students come forward to give their speeches, they know they will be in front of the class for exactly thirty seconds. If they run out of things to say (and most won't) they must stay up in front and try to think of something else to add to their speech to fill the time. I do this to help students learn to think on their feet. Of course, I prompt them with a comment if they need it. If they run long, they get cut off. Most kids are surprised at just how fast thirty seconds goes by.

My goals are many in asking students to speak: to not be afraid to be in front of people, to stay composed, to talk without notes off the top of their heads, to tell us what they know confidently, and to get a sense of how fast time can go while speaking. When I introduce public speaking to students, I often use the same example of how easy it can be. As I was talking with a student a few years back, she began telling me about her Mexican heritage. She talked for at least five minutes right off the top of her head. And she didn't need notecards! Students have knowledge to share—this is their chance, so they should go for it!

After thirty-second speeches, most students beg for a longer period of time, and many want to go first the next time. The next step is a forty-five-second speech, where kids get to choose their own topics and can prepare their thoughts overnight. When they come to class the next day, they still get ten to fifteen minutes to prepare and make props, but they also still cannot use notecards. Some examples of student-chosen topics are how to tie shoelaces, how to throw a football, or how to play a board game. Some become hilarious, some are more serious. But all are respected. Students learn that we are all there to support each other and gain more and more composure in front of an audience. They also gain confidence that shows up in other ways throughout the year. And they keep asking for longer speeches! You can't beat that.

There are plenty of concepts to base a teaching approach on—creativity, openness, love or respect, to name just a few. The goal of my approach at the beginning of the year is to set students up for success. While most of these ideas were not written into in my classroom management plan for my education program, one thing I am certain of is this: starting out with concepts that include *heart* help students flourish.

Chapter 4

Room Dynamics

"Instead of asking us to get in line,
you should just ask us to get in clumps,
because that's what we do anyway."
Ella, 4th grader

I've come to believe that my educational philosophy and classroom management can be integrated and combined to create something bigger than both, something I call "room dynamics." I truly believe 75% of the time a lesson doesn't go as planned, or I become frustrated with students behaving in ways contrary to my expectations, it is because my classroom dynamic was flawed.

Most education certification programs have their teacher candidates create their education philosophy and classroom management plan. This is a necessary step in formulating a vision for the classroom. But it's one thing to come up with a plan before becoming a full-time teacher; it's a whole other thing to fine tune, or even blow up, the original plan after experiencing a real classroom of students. While in my education program, I came up with a plan that included engaging activities and deep thinking. But it was limited. I didn't know my ideas would merge into something more.

I've come to believe the entire learning/teaching process can be put into terms of relationships. And those relationships are tied directly to room dynamics. Of course, building relationships between students, parents and myself, as well as building student-to-student relationships, is key; this entire book is about those kinds of relationships. Functioning interpersonal relationships set the tone for how people relate in the classroom. Are we all supportive, kind, forgiving and light-hearted? Do we encourage a classroom environment in which making errors is okay? Or are people overly competitive, reactionary, mean-spirited, and humiliating? A teacher has a lot to do with setting this tone early in the year. Throughout the years, I've done well in many cases, and have had to improve in others.

Three additional relationships described in this chapter are different than the interpersonal ones people usually think about. Relationships between people are the majority of the issue, but there are other relationships as well. If my students don't buy into things in the classroom, it may not matter that I have a great lesson planned or have a great system for signing in for hot lunch; there may be too much chaos or apathy to make things work the way I designed them.

The other relationships that are almost as important as interpersonal are: 1. how students relate to systems within the class, 2. how students relate to the environment and materials in the room, and 3. how they relate to lessons during the learning experience. The systems set up in the room guide the structure, the environment sets the tone of comfort and accessibility, while the lessons guide the learning. How students relate and engage with these three factors transforms good learning into great learning.

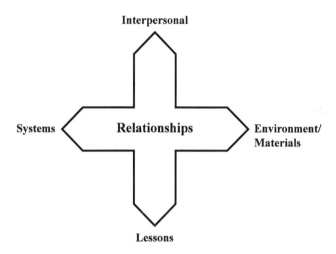

Systems

By systems, I mean procedures and other ways the classroom is set up to function. Systems in the classroom might include how the day is scheduled, how students transition between subjects or classes, jobs created in the room or the myriad of other ways the day is structured. How do kids relate to systems? Do the systems make sense to the students? Have I explained the reasons for each system, or had any input from students? Are the systems fair? Do they have to be?

How do I take attendance? Is it an old-fashioned way where I call out names? Can I have children assigned to the job? Can I make it more of a teachable moment? Is there a way I can incorporate math into the process, maybe keeping track of attendance on a running graph to make a line graph?

There are hundreds of questions I can ask myself. I can't provide all the answers to these questions, but thinking about them can help guide a classroom vision and plan for a highly effective learning environment. Other system questions to consider include:

1. What can be made into a tradition that kids will enjoy being a part of, even if it is a formal procedure?
2. How is lunch count taken, for hot or cold lunch?
3. When do students sharpen pencils?
4. How about getting drinks and bathroom breaks?
5. What do students do when they first walk in the room?
6. How is seating arranged?
7. Can students sit with friends?
8. Do they have to sit with at least one girl and one boy at a table?
9. How is late or missing homework handled?
10. Who is responsible for making sure students receive missed work—students or the teacher?
11. Is there a bin for missed work?
12. How can student mailboxes be used?
13. Is there a point system for homework? Should there be?

14. Are incentives or rewards offered? Should they be?

15. How is homework graded? Is it weighted?

16. What kind of take-home folders are used for homework?

17. Can you make grading something kids can help with?

18. How is handing back homework handled?

19. Are points given for homework being turned in, or for tests being signed by parents and returned?

20. Do students ever use self-assessments?

21. How are interruptions handled, whether funny or serious?

22. Do kids have to be in lines?

23. How are they lined up? Alphabetically, or by student number? Does it matter?

24. Are students required to shake hands when they enter?

25. What about celebrations of learning?

26. Is there a "classroom constitution" or some other charter/commitment tool? Is it referred to?

27. What if it's not followed?

As you can see, there might be no end to the systems questions a teacher can ask. But the answers to these questions can help the classroom run more smoothly.

An experience at one school demonstrates the concept of systems very well. Being new to the school, I wanted to set the tone of togetherness in my new fifth grade classroom—we had a small group meeting in the morning, and also had desks arranged for students to be in small groups of four, all facing each other when seated. But this group had a hard time focusing on almost any activity at the beginning of the year; as a group, they didn't possess a lot of classroom self-control. Most just did not have the ability to behave appropriately while seated in groups. So, of course it caused me stress trying to manage the class.

The point of the story is this: my approach of grouping students in fours didn't help them behave properly. My seating arrangement (a system) was beyond their capabilities at that time of the year; these students could not relate to the system. I should have recognized this quickly and adjusted, but I didn't. After some time in a classroom, discerning where adjustment is needed can be done more quickly. While I practice patience with the dynamics of the classroom, there are also times I can tell immediately that something is not right. The job for kids is to learn; if something I've planned gets in the way of that, I need to be flexible enough to change.

There are plenty of other systems I've seen or tried in the classroom: using student self-evaluation sheets to be signed by parents over the weekend, point systems for behavior in math class, or green/yellow/red behavior signs for students. Some of them are effective, many aren't. Systems that students relate to and also learn from are the goal. This can eliminate frustration and will make students more responsible for themselves.

Environment and Materials

Students also have relationships with both the environment and the materials in class. A classroom should be designed with warmth in mind, but also with function. It's great to have lots of color, pillows, and items for them to explore. It's also important that the materials are accessible. If students need to use protractors, books, rulers, and all the other supplies needed to be a good student, are these items easy for students to get access to? Sometimes these types of things get lost in the shuffle of worrying about other things in the room, like keeping students engaged or getting them lined up to get to another class. It's very easy to let things slip away during the school year. So many things get piled on a teacher's plate during the year that sometimes the environment and materials get overlooked or just neglected. Planning better before the school year starts can make a huge difference.

Here are a few questions I ask myself. Are protractors and pencils in a good spot for students to use? Are rulers tucked away on a shelf where students don't really see them, or are they in a visible spot? Just this past summer, I had to rearrange something for the new school year. Last year, my classroom had flexible tape measures stuffed in glass jars; students rarely chose to use them. For this school year, I found a coat rack that was being thrown away and placed it in my room, with those same tape measures hanging and available for use. I bet they'll be used more in this coming year, without me even saying a word about them.

I've also had to look at my use of wall space, stuffed animals, rugs, reference books and computers. And throughout the year, I adjust to make the way I use them most effective for learning.

A list of questions I ask myself about the environment and the materials I provide might include:

1. How are textbooks handled? Do students keep all books in a desk or are books stored in lockers or on shelves?
2. How about creating different areas for different books?
3. Do I have colors in the room that liven up the place?
4. Should I have a couch or comfortable reading chair in the room?
5. How easy is it for students to interact with science or math manipulatives?
6. Can they bring something from home (stuffed animal, photos, etc.) to make the room feel more comfortable, without taking away from academics?
7. Are there too many plastic or metal bins?
8. Could more natural materials be used?
9. Is there a place where kids can lay down to read instead of just sitting at desks?

I've had to really take a look at my classroom, and at times have thought to myself, "Why did I set things up that way?" Sometimes, I even have to get down on my knees to look around the room from a shorter perspective. If I really think about it, and see things from student's perspective, it helps tremendously in how students relate to the environment and materials.

Lesson Design

Lessons can make or break a teacher and the learning process for students. This is huge. It's so important, I almost don't know where to start. In the palm of a teacher's hand is the power to bore students to death with dull, old-fashioned, sleep-inducing lessons, or to make learning fun, engaging and challenging with incredible lessons. Believe it or not, students have a relationship with your lessons.

I was an excellent student in elementary school, always doing what the teacher wanted; I never got in trouble and respected my teachers (except when my temper got the best of me during athletic competition). I was the "good kid." But an example from my sixth grade demonstrates what even a "good kid" will do when bored or with too much time on his hands.

After finishing a spelling exam early, I decided to draw in my notebook while others finished. As the time went on, one thing lead to another and, without me even thinking about what I was doing, I ended up drawing something inappropriate. As others were still working, my teacher looked over at me and came over to see what I was drawing. My teacher was shocked to see what I had drawn and I was shocked to get caught. Being a scared little kid, I initially tried to blame someone else. But of course, I knew there was no one else to blame. I was scared to death she would tell my parents, but all she did was talk to me after school.

Now that I see things from a teacher's perspective, that young Peter was somewhat set up to get in trouble. Not that the teacher could keep me occupied 100% of the time, but I really had no intention of doing something wrong when I was finished with that spelling test. As a kid, I just drifted into it. That experience stuck with me.

This is an example of a good student getting into trouble because he was bored and had too much time to wait for others. What can we do to help keep our students' attention from wandering? While we can't expect to keep students from drifting from time to time, we can try our best to keep them successful.

It doesn't happen often, but I've had students come right out and tell me when they're bored. I tell them upfront that my job is for them to learn, not be entertained, but I do think about their comments, too. Not *all* lessons are going to be worthy of Academy Awards for Comedic Performance.

I've also had students so involved with lessons and the fun they are having that they groan when time runs out. Creativity in the classroom can change students' views of school, themselves, and their ideas about what they can accomplish and learn. That is a huge responsibility.

Boredom in a classroom comes in many varieties: a teacher who is a windbag, a book that is outdated or lessons that are too slow, too irrelevant, too easy, too still, too whatever. Even ideal students will talk out, doodle or find other ways to keep their minds and spirits occupied if they are bored or unchallenged. That's one reason I make most of my lessons at least somewhat entertaining or mysterious.

Do students relate to what I'm talking about? Do I make the lessons fun? Are they interactive? Can students be talkative? Are things challenging? Am I only teaching from a book? Do students ever get outside the classroom? Do I make things relevant to their world? Do I have the students using any current technology? Are my lessons affirming? A teacher can ask all of these questions—and more—when designing lessons. When students are internally answering these questions, and externally behaving their answers, they are forming relationships with lessons. Either students are connecting or they aren't. If they aren't, whose fault is that?

There have been plenty of times when students have not done what I wanted them to do in the middle of a lesson—they may not have discussed things the way I hoped, used teamwork, or tried as hard as I would have liked. Is this really their fault? Most of the time, it's probably not. When students don't follow my vision for their learning, I try not to get too frustrated with them. If something goes awry, I usually blame it on a flaw in my lesson, not on the students. There are ways to improve lesson design to motivate to students to want to tackle things in a fun, responsible way.

Good lesson design uses student energy as a positive asset to the learning experience. One example is deciding how much we want students to talk in our classes. Many times, teachers want students to be quiet. I'm guilty of it, too. We want students' attention for instruction, directions and focus. Ask students and most will say teachers are always telling them to be quiet. That's because kids like to talk—even though teachers have something to say!

But there's nothing wrong with students who want to talk. Don't blame them for wanting to do something that comes naturally to them. Instead of designing lessons where students are constantly reminded to be quiet, design lessons so that students can use their talkativeness in a positive way. In a lesson on latitude and longitude, I may let students guide each other around a globe or map using coordinates. In a lesson on 6+1 writing traits, I have students write a story together and then share their story and the trait they used with the class. In a math lesson, I ask students for the numbers to use for practice problems written on the board during a full group lesson. These are simple ways to allow students the chance to talk during lessons. It only makes sense to let kids talk, but it takes a determined teacher to keep designing lessons that use student talkativeness as an asset in the classroom. It sounds so simple and obvious, but it's not used enough.

As my professor Casey O'Keefe stressed in her developmental literacy class, "Students need to verbalize to internalize" (O'Keefe, 2002). This is so true, and really mixes well with the use of Bloom's Taxonomy. Students who are only working with the internal, self-talk section of their minds seem to have a harder time telling you their thinking or extending their learning. Students who consistently discuss their learning with others can explain things and articulate their thinking better and make better connections. And if they can't, not letting them talk isn't going to help them. Think about it: if we really want students to articulate their thinking, how does not letting them talk help with that? Teachers do need students' attention, and there are plenty of times I myself ask students to be quiet, but we have to design lessons differently. Kids want to engage; help them out by improving lesson design.

And when we think about students talking, we will want them to use terms we use in class. Even with that goal, it's easy for teachers to talk too much. An example of this might help here. In a certain lesson on improper fractions, I wanted to have students use the term "improper fraction," but I caught myself being the only one actually saying the term; students weren't using it. I'd say something like, "Give me an example of an improper fraction." It takes an adept teacher to phrase questions and guide discussions in a way that influences students to talk and use terms so they are saying them, instead of just hearing the teacher say them. Instead of asking, "Who can tell me which of these is an improper fraction?" a teacher could say, "What type of number is this?" In this way, students have to use the word "improper fraction" and not just hear it from the teacher. Watch yourself and others; it's amazing how often teachers are using terms and the students are not.

Using students' natural talkativeness as a positive is only one way to improve lesson design. As teachers in training, we learn to create lessons according to some well-tested structures. We learn to include an introductory teaser, objectives, instruction, modeling, guided and independent practice and some culminating activity. But there is so much more to lesson design, and our early teaching preparations can only really expose us to so much, without the stress of being with a real classroom full of students.

On the way into my classroom many years ago, a coworker stopped me to say that her fourth grade daughter loved being in my class. I thanked her and then went about my day. But a couple of days later, I decided to ask my colleague why her daughter said that. I was curious to know why she loved being in my class and that maybe I could use this information to improve. My colleague said her daughter never knew what to expect in class; her daughter was intrigued to see what I would come up with next, and what would happen in school each day. It wasn't that the classroom didn't have structure or a schedule that she was used to; it did. But the schedule and structure didn't set the tone of the day. Learning experiences did.

Whether I planned to make it that way or not, I don't quite know. I think it was a by-product of not over-planning everything weeks ahead of time, but coming up with timely, unique, creative ways for students to interact with the lessons. It also came from being open to knowing that student learning may alter my initial plans.

There have been plenty of times where I've been stymied as to what would be the best way to teach something; how can I have students really understand, versus have them only gain fleeting, superficial understanding? I guess I've learned to trust that my creativity will "answer the call." I don't depend solely on these kinds of spontaneous ideas, but I do count on them coming to me from time to time. I've noticed literally changing my perspective works for me: lying down seems to help my creativity. It's helped me to the point where I've wondered if there's ever been research done on the creative/thinking process while people are horizontal versus vertical. I've even had my students lie down on the classroom floor, and sometimes it does seem to help kick-start their creativity.

Some examples of using creativity to enhance lessons might help here. While teaching students about liquid volume, why not actually use liquid? Although this sounds so logical, I didn't always use obvious approaches. I now find a place in the room that can get messy, use a bucket of water and have students pour water from one container to another, speaking the terms of volume, and trying not to spill. Of course they do, and that is expected. Or, while teaching latitude, I have kids tape a string to the middle of a round table, as if it's the middle of the earth. The edge of the round table then becomes the equator. Students are instructed to lift the string to a certain degree above the surface to create an angle from the middle of the earth. As they rotate the free end of the string around the table, they are creating a north latitude line around the globe. I mix this in with showing them a real globe and how the imaginary line they just created above the table is just like the line on the globe (i.e., thirty degrees north).

One other component of lesson planning that helps create engaging lessons is the use of "forward thinking", which isn't anything new. I try to foresee questions and thoughts that students may have. Students will ask many "what if" questions. Can I prepare for all of them? No, but foresight can help take some of their questions and let them lead to unexplored teachable moments, some that will thrill both them and me.

Not everything I am teaching students has to be a direct lesson. Some things will be learned better as a matter of course in the classroom. In fact, this type of learning is seamless and subconscious. But it requires planning and a vision. I can set up systems and strategies in the room that are fun and engaging without kids even knowing the long-term goals involved. An example is the copy of a large protractor we use in a game based on Bingo that we call Mathingo. I don't explain the use of the protractor at all as I pass out the game board, which contains the image of a large protractor. I have students draw lines from the vertex to certain degrees to create different zones on their paper. I use this strategy to get students to practice using protractors before we ever get to using them in a pure lesson.

In another example, I stack several boxes of Jell-O on a table and ask the kids what they think the boxes have to do with social studies. Their guesses are priceless. I then switch gears to start to talk about American government, sharing with them how decisions are made, how representatives are chosen, how laws are created and how trials work. All of this is accomplished while the Jell-O boxes stay put on the table. Of course, by the end of the lesson, students start putting together that J is for the Judicial branch, E is for the Executive and L is for the Legislative.

There are plenty of ways to be creative in your lessons. In addition to all the objectives you have and the practice students need, there are other things to think about. Some questions I ask myself or ideas to think about while planning lessons are:

1. How can I get kids to talk during a lesson?

2. What do I do if the talking gets out of control?

3. Can I build a way for students to know when to stop, like using a timer?

4. Should I use a book in this lesson, or are there ways I can integrate movement or other materials to enhance the lesson?

5. Could I create stations for students to move between?

6. How could I add some humorous aspect to the lesson?
(Find a cartoon on Google, challenge students to use some creativity in their answers, etc.).

Finding answers to these questions can help you create lessons that engage students and improve the relationships students have with the material you are presenting. Room dynamics are based on relationships with systems, the physical environment and materials, and lessons. We spend so much time building interpersonal relationships; if we take that same approach to room dynamics, students will connect much better to what is happening in class. And with that connection comes improved learning.

Chapter 5

Reflective Teaching

When is the last time you learned something that really took you out of your comfort zone? And I mean *really* stretched you so much that you were anxious all day? Every teacher should have to experience what I did during one summer break—smashing through a fear. Saying "a" fear here does not explain it well enough; "biggest" fear would be more accurate. I don't know if we all have that one hidden fear of something that we'd like to do but have always talked ourselves out of, but I imagine most of us have at least one. Mine was always acting on stage as an adult. Being involved in an elementary school production didn't count; the acting had to be on stage, multiple times, with many lines to remember.

I can't quite figure out why acting gave me so much anxiety, but it did. It's not like I'm scared of talking in front of people; in fact, I like the chance to give speeches even if it makes me somewhat anxious. And I like performing in front of people, too—I used to love playing sports in front of a crowd. But acting is different—I'd have to remember lines, have other people counting on me to do my part and show a certain level of vulnerability that's different from other forms of being in front of a crowd. I guess that's why it always scared me, like I couldn't trust myself to remember my lines or let people see me in that vulnerable of a position.

So why did I decide to do a play one summer? The reasons are many. Mostly I wanted to meet new people and get out of the house during my summer off from teaching. And after discussing things with a friend, we decided to commit to each other to do the opposite of our same old, boring routine in an effort to make our lives better. My summer became the Summer of Snake (an old basketball nickname of mine), where I changed my attitude and actions to get different results. This was based on the character of George on *"Seinfeld,"* in which George does the opposite of what he normally does in his sorry life to get a date.

For me, the process of following through with my commitment to act in a play totally changed me. It's made me see the world differently, helped me learn more about the learning process and the power of my own mind, taught me new vocabulary, and forced me to break old comfort zones. It also helped me understand what it takes to get through anxiety and other emotions, and will help me to be a better, more empathetic teacher. Although I did not freak out, and did learn my lines, there was a certain uncertainty involved in the process. I even called "rehearsal" a "practice" the first night, which seemed out of place. I generally felt out of my element.

As I thought about the process I was going through, it made me think about how my students might feel if they don't quite get something or don't feel comfortable in their own skin or ability. It also brought to mind some irrational fears I had as an elementary student. One of those fears was of performing at a school dance during an ice cream social. I had really wanted to be part of the dance group, but wasn't chosen by my teacher. When my parents and I arrived at the ice cream social, my teacher asked me to replace a student who couldn't make it that night. My frightened response was to say no, so I didn't perform. I still remember the incident forty years later. My internal fears haven't made a lot of sense; that is for sure! Have yours? They may not for students either, but that doesn't mean their fears aren't real.

Joining the cast of the play brought up some of these memories that should help me relate this experience to my students. Although I was on stage for a total of about ten minutes and only had about twenty-five lines, I found myself coming up with all kinds of mental strategies to help me remember lines: relying on key first words of each line, remembering that each line of dialogue pertains to something of the story, thinking about the flow of the scene, and visualizing the script and the setting. Since my heart was pounding before I walked on stage (even during rehearsal), I thought it might be good for me to practice my lines when my heart was at a higher rate. So, instead of practicing my lines while sitting at home, I started practicing my lines while hiking through a forest. All of these strategies came to me as I was struggling to handle the mind games I played with myself and the anxiety I felt.

Am I crazy, or do other people go through these types of things, too? I had a feeling I was not alone in my struggles. What struck me about the learning process of being in a play was how similar it might be to how my struggling students feel and what their brains might be trying to do. For instance, learning math introduces a barrage of different procedures, processes and concepts. For every one rule you get, there seems to come another five or six. To struggling math students, it's got to be tiring, frustrating and frightening, this relentless onslaught of things to learn. Going through these feelings during the play, and the thoughts that came with them, gave me a new perspective on what it means to learn something that isn't coming easy. And I wondered: as a reflective teacher, can I take some of the mental strategies I used to memorize lines to help my math students become better thinkers, and possibly reduce some anxiety, too?

Because some of these students may already be struggling mentally, adding to their internal pressure is not the goal. But are there other strategies I can teach them? Can this experience make me more real and human with my students? I wanted to take the experience and talk with my students, relate to them as a feeling, honest human being, and let them know that even adults have to struggle sometimes to learn and grow.

During the process, I also found that just memorizing lines in my head was okay, but trying to get them correct in front of my cast mates was tougher. What was there in this process that could help me help my students? Maybe practicing in context and out loud would be more beneficial than just doing work alone or as homework. It once again reminded me of my professor's saying, "Verbalize to internalize." If learning lines improved in context with the world and others, what would happen if I had students learn math in context and out loud? Could I take math procedures and concepts and pour them into contextual situations in the classroom? Could I incorporate authentic uses to replace standard lessons? I thought so.

In one scene of my play, I had to deliver several lines and draw back from another actor, telling him he looked like Boris Karloff. He then was supposed to attack me. Immediately prior to this action, I was supposed to have responded to a couple of other lines from another actor. That other actor sometimes skipped ahead and forced me to jump into my Boris Karloff line a little prematurely. During early rehearsals, we stopped mid-scene to correct this very minor error. During dress rehearsal, it happened again, and I had to decide whether to stop the scene to correct it or just move on and rattle off my next line. I decided not to stop and just say my Boris Karloff line. This decision happened in my brain in a split second. It amazes me that my brain could do that, even in the midst of being nervous and on stage. I want to pass this fascination with the power of our brains onto my students, especially insecure students. I want them to believe that their minds also have the capacity to do amazing things.

The other aspect of the play that really affected me was the process of breaking down old comfort zones and creating new ones. At the beginning of the process, the entire acting scene was new and scary to me; after going through the process, it turned into the opposite, one of awe and fun. Well, at least, mostly fun. Each day seemed like I was conquering just a little bit more of some kind of anxiety, and thereby creating a broader comfort zone for myself, with new people, with new experiences, and with handling my emotions. I wanted to take this experience and use it to really connect with my new students, to help them understand that fears do not have to stop them from learning new things, that courage is not living without fear, and that they can trust me to empathize with them in their struggles. This is the kind of teaching and relating that I think can change a classroom.

My acting story reminds me of a time a student chose to do something new and possibly scary. As a class, my fourth graders were going to present a math dance to the rest of the school, to the tune of Pink's song, "Get This Party Started." Most of the students wanted to do it and readily volunteered with enthusiasm. One student very much wanted to do the dance, but at the same time was very hesitant. Fear of doing something out of his comfort zone was keeping him from committing to being part of the dance performance. He was procrastinating, and I allowed him some time to decide. He just couldn't get through his internal anxiety about doing it. On a Friday, he finally decided not to do it, and that was okay with me. But the following Monday he came into class and announced he had changed his mind. When the time came to do the dance in front of the school, he did it. It was thrilling to see him on stage; seeing a student crush an obstacle is awesome!

In the National Football League, announcers and rookies are often quoted as saying the speed of the professional game is much faster than the speed of the collegiate game. After a year or two in the league, we hear players say that the game slows down for them. What I think they mean is that they started to feel more comfortable with the speed; what they saw and experienced didn't come at them and their brains quite as fast as it had originally. This is how I felt in the play, and I finally acknowledged just how useful the analogy was for all learning. I think about when I first learned to drive a car. The first time I pulled into a gas station to fill up the tank, during a driving lesson, I had to inch in very slowly, not knowing quite how to turn into the right spot. Now I do it without even thinking about it. Race car drivers must have the same "slowing down" of things in their field, even if they are going two hundred miles per hour.

How can we use this analogy of things seeming fast, but slowing down after we become more comfortable to help our students? One way is to discuss this type of thing, to get the idea out in the open. But another is to demonstrate how things get easier or "slower" even if they are very hard or "fast" at the start of the learning process. I remind students all the time of where they came from in their learning. Whether it is in the use of a protractor or in designing a box, we look back at the initial stages and laugh at how hard it was then, compared to how easy it is now.

As you can see, personal experiences can change our approach to teaching. What have you been thinking about doing, but haven't had the guts to try yet? My advice: go do it! Taking courageous steps may help more people than just ourselves.

Chapter 6

Parents

After the Native American
sleepover and presentation in early fall:
*"We don't usually see this type of demonstration
until spring. Where did you come from?"*
Parent of 4th grader

When starting out in teaching, there are plenty of things to juggle throughout the year—students to get to know, curriculum to understand, lessons to design, room dynamics to put in place and experiment with, school procedures to learn, and other teachers to meet. In addition to all of these factors, there is another key ingredient to a good year of teaching: relationships with parents.

Working with parents is an aspect of teaching that isn't mentioned very often in teacher certification programs, but it's a big part of a teacher's job, so it needs to be discussed. Relationships with parents can be very supportive and meaningful, but they can also be challenging at times. To talk only about challenges would be unfair to the parents who support teachers in so many ways, as room parents, chaperones, room cleaners, drivers, or even letter writers. Therefore, I hope to provide some balanced insight on building relationships with these very important people.

Although teaching has felt like my calling, some aspects of the profession have been harder for me than others. My early years were filled with much soul-searching and self-talk, both good and bad. Part of the soul-searching left me with self-doubt in "dealing" with parents of students. *But this self-doubt and my perception of parents was not their fault at all*; it was all my own "stuff"—inexperience, misperceptions, and insecurity.

All of this "stuff" crept in, leading me to think I had to "deal" with parents. Fortunately, two comments from other teachers helped change my perspective. One teacher said, "Parents are just looking out for their children, which is what they are supposed to be doing." Another colleague mentioned that I should look at it from a different perspective—not one of "dealing" with parents but of "working" with parents. Both of these comments changed me as a teacher, and as a communicator. I began to let parents see my heart in much the same way I did with students. By revealing my heart with sincerity to parents, they began to realize not only did my classroom have rigor and high expectations, but it had much more. As I pondered this chapter, I began to wonder how my heart for students and learning corresponded with the heart parents have for their children, and how I could relate this to a teacher's work.

Simple Communication

Going into a new year, everyone has plenty of expectations and visualizations of what the year will look like. For most teachers, parents of new students are an unknown variable. It's easy for teachers to wonder how the interactions will occur, and if they will be constructive. Parents want the best for their children, and teachers want the best for all children, too. If that is truly the case, then teachers must demonstrate it in a way parents can trust.

Parents want honest and fair feedback on their children's learning and behavior, but it goes deeper than that. They want to know you know their children, and that their children are in good, capable hands. They want to know you have their children's best interest in mind by becoming aware of strengths, areas of improvement, special abilities or talents, and what makes their children "tick." This may not always be easy, especially when there are so many kids in a classroom, but it can be done if it is a priority.

The other thing parents are really looking for is an understanding that what they will get from you as their children's teacher is competent instruction and guidance in the subjects you will be teaching them. For me, as an upper elementary teacher, I think the parents of my students want me to prepare their children for the next grade; they want to know their children will be ready for fifth grade or beyond in math, that they're reading at or above grade level and that their writing is progressing at a good pace. I integrate math, reading, writing, social studies and science in a variety of ways, but what it comes down to is how far am I progressing students toward where they need to be as they grow up? If students demonstrate their progress in these areas, parents will be happy. If not, I'll hear about it, and I should hear about it. If I'm not helping students progress appropriately, then something about my instruction needs to change.

When starting at a new school, be it as a veteran teacher or one brand new to the profession, a teacher has no reputation or relationship with parents. Although it would be nice to arrive with a good reputation and relationships already built, it just doesn't happen that way; both take time to develop. This is where professionalism and maturity make a difference.

Teachers must let parents know we have the well-being of their children in mind, and at heart, in everything we do in the room, which is not an easy task. One way teachers can do this is by communicating long-term goals. Not all activities in a classroom will give the impression that great learning is occurring at a specific moment of time, but when looked at from a wider, long-term perspective, things make much more sense. While this communication of goals may be wonderful in theory, the reality is that communicating to parents is not always easy, especially if parents have limited involvement. Does that mean we don't try? Not at all.

I've learned having a meeting with parents at the beginning of the year to lay out my philosophy and structure of the class is imperative. Not only can I explain myself, and answer parents' questions, but they also get a chance to see my professionalism and passion for teaching. During the meeting, I communicate to parents the school's schedule, special dates to remember, and a summary of topics covered during the year, but I also share a lot more. I also explain my background, my heart for teaching by demonstrating the gong, the "Know" graphic depicting the learning process, my methods and what I'm trying to accomplish as I use them. It also gives me the chance to stress the one main goal: student learning. I explain my job is not to have students earn A's or exceed some type of expectations or criteria. Although these aspects can be important and are indirect results of effective teaching, students are in the classroom to learn and develop as much as they can, in the best ways they can. Especially at the elementary level, I emphasize that it's most important for students to progress, rather than earn something external to themselves.

At my school, in addition to having a parent information meeting, we have "listening" conferences in the first weeks of school. In these meetings, parents have the opportunity to tell me what they'd like me to know about their children, and I listen. During these conferences, I want to know whatever they are comfortable telling me—whether it has to do with the death of the family dog, family information that is relevant, sicknesses, subjects in which their children excel or struggle, social issues to be aware of, or anything else pertinent to knowing their children.

This hasn't been the standard way of doing things at other schools where I have taught, so these meetings make my school special in this regard. But I want to stress that even if a school doesn't require these listening conferences or parent information meetings, there are ways to symbolically let parents know you want to connect with them and have a heart for their children. Contacting parents via letter, email, or phone can go a long way in communicating important aspects of the year: a teacher introduction, the plan for the year, long-term goals and a heart for their children.

I know this sounds too easy, because not all parents are available by any of these avenues. For those parents, simple gestures make a difference—shaking their hands when you see them is an acknowledgment that they may not receive very often. How hard is it to offer a handshake? All teachers can do this. Also, asking parents about things students bring up in class or in a conversation is a good way to connect. But what about those parents you just don't see? Going to student games or checking in about a sick child are two other ways teachers can show concern for students and it lets parents know you care.

When parents ask their child how the school day went, many get the standard response: "Fine." Even if we acknowledge that this happens, wouldn't it be great if what was going on in the classroom was so cool, that students wanted to share with their parents? Children often have a way of letting their parents know they have an effective teacher—they sneak in comments about something that was brought up in class, or show an enthusiasm for school that they may not have shown before. They may also talk about an inside joke from the day, or some crazy thing a teacher did or said. This, too, can be considered communicating with parents—in fact, it's probably the most effective way.

These are all examples of communicating when there are no issues with student's behavior or academic achievement. But not all communication is this easy. There are times when teachers have to communicate concerns about a student. And there are plenty of times when students tell a biased narrative of what happened in a classroom or leave out important information that would change a parent's perception of the classroom. What then? One of the things I've had to learn is how to go from thinking I had to be politically correct to being compassionately honest about students with their parents. Parents deserve the truth, no matter how hard it may be to inform them of a concern. Also, before jumping to conclusions or taking things personally when a parent wants to talk with me, I make sure to get as much information as I can by listening to what they've heard or understand to be the truth.

I may need to step out of my comfort zone or stretch myself in other ways too. A teacher's day is long. A teacher is "on" most of the day, and it can be darn grueling. Sometimes, the last thing I want to do is talk to a parent. I'm worn out and my mood is not the greatest for having a frank conversation, or being empathetic. All of these are true. But communication is a vital element of being an effective teacher.

My best strategy for this is to schedule talks or meetings with parents at times of the day that will work best for both of us. Some days, early morning before classes start is the best. This way, the conversation happens before I'm worn out by the day. But I'm not a morning person, and like to get to school early when it's quiet to get prepared for the day, so this time is not always the easiest for me. For this reason, most of my scheduled times to talk with parents are after school. Yes, I may be more worn out, but, since I feel my most important job is teaching students, I want to save the best of my energy for the time that I am with students. Conversations with parents can take place outside of that time. Each teacher has to find his or her own solution for incorporating time with parents.

It's my job to teach children, and communicating with parents effectively is part of the process. Trying to juggle my own need for some sanity with the need to be a communicator is not easy. I may need to be creative with this process, but striving to be courteous, available and informative is a start.

Differing Perspectives

> While eating lunch in the classroom,
> seeing an 11-year-old rip her food
> with her hands instead of using a knife.
> *"I don't know how to use a knife.*
> *My dad cuts everything for me."*
> Lisa, 5th grader

Since we all experience the world in varying ways, parents may have different perspectives on children and learning. Some parents may let things go more than I would, or it may go the other way, and they may be stricter than I am. Yes, parents might handle things differently than I might handle them. This is natural and must be understood.

There are plenty of things affecting other people that I need to be aware of, or at least try to understand. Parents can be dealing with any number of things: work stresses, family problems or just everyday living challenges. I've had parents dealing with their child's cancer diagnosis and even a death of a child. Although I've thought that nothing should get in the way of a student's learning in the classroom, in reality other things do sometimes trump short-term learning. Death, sickness, divorce, relationships—all of these things put classroom lessons into a different perspective. They should alter our empathy and how we work with students and parents.

Because we all see the world in varied ways, teachers need to cultivate congruent views of the classroom and of learning by outlining clear, consistent expectations for behavior and academics. Showing respect for parent perceptions and respecting their wishes is also a must. Showing flexibility to others' needs is very helpful in the long-run.

Different perspectives materialize because of many factors. High stressors can alter someone's perspective, but so can their level of information. Some of this will be positive, some will not. At my first school, there was a telling example of how parents can have one perspective of a situation, but then can switch their thinking. During this year, when one girl tried to hide during a morning meeting, the other students announced it to me. I called her out on it and let her know that her behavior was unacceptable. When this student's parents came in for conferences, her dad was upset with me because he had been told I was upset with his daughter for no reason. I listened to his concern but then discussed the hiding incident. After hearing the entire story, the father understood the situation, and the mood of the conference became warmer. Perspectives are often times miscommunications. And miscommunications can be solved with awareness and effort. With planning, forethought and open communication, almost any misunderstanding can be smoothed out.

Part of my learning process has been working with parents both in the private and public school setting. Sometimes parents at private schools are more involved because they're paying for the schooling, but that's not always the case. While we may see things differently, we all still do have the same emphasis on student learning. Because of this, communicating our goals and the expectations we have of students can go a long way in preventing miscommunications or in removing barriers to understanding.

Positive Outcomes

Honestly, I have had a good share of affirming acknowledgments from parents, but I have also had my share of questioning parents and tough meetings. I have found the best way to connect with them is to listen. After listening, I usually get a chance to share my own reasoning or perspective. From there, parents and I become active participants in solving what might be a stressful situation. The following story illustrates what can happen when listening is combined with effective teaching.

While working at an urban school, I was in charge of an enrichment program at recess for students who needed support in math. Since the school had many student teachers, they helped me run the program by teaching students grouped by age in different rooms for about twenty minutes. As you can imagine, since the program was run at recess and students were required to be there two or three times per week, some of them were not too thrilled to be there and skipped the extra sessions to go outside.

During one semester, a student teacher informed me that one student was skipping the program and needed some kind of consequence to be more committed to getting to the classroom at recess. I usually talked with their homeroom teachers about consequences for missing the support sessions. This time I decided to send a letter home, informing the student's parent of his absences from the support sessions. The letter also explained that he was being held in for more recesses to catch him up on the math that he missed. After writing the letter, but before sending it, this student's homeroom teacher approached me and asked if that was a wise thing to do, since this mother was very assertive. I pondered the homeroom teacher's comment, but I still sent the letter.

The next morning while I was co-teaching in another classroom, I was called out in the hallway to be confronted by this parent, who was not happy with me for sending her the letter. Specifically, she was not happy that she hadn't heard about it sooner. Of course, being confronted like this got my defenses up and I was flustered, but I did keep my composure. I listened to her and let her know I thought she had a point. I apologized and asked her to help me with the situation. She did talk with her son, and things got somewhat better that year.

But that wasn't the end of the story. During the next year, I had her older son in my sixth grade math class. After seeing how I taught and that her son loved my math class, she went out of her way two or three times during the school year to let me know she appreciated my work. She may have intimidated other teachers, but she was very affirming and supportive of me. She knew I wanted the best for her children and knew what I was capable of. But it took time, effort and quality teaching.

Prior to that year, at another school, a colleague told me the parent of a new student might be challenging on some issues. I heard her thoughts, but waited to form an opinion. Fortunately, I did not let the information influence my teaching, or my relationship with the student or parent. What I found was my experience with this parent was the opposite of the other teacher's. Since I had not let the biased information affect my teaching, the parent ended up being one of my greatest supporters during that school year. When I left the school, she gave me a very nice gift with a handwritten note of thanks. From this example, I've learned to form my own opinions based on personal interactions with students and families.

After receiving copies
of affirmative letters from parents,
*"You don't usually hear those
kind of affirmations until you're dead!"*
Linda, my co-teacher

Working with parents can be rewarding, too. Teachers don't get enough compliments, but getting one from a parent has changed my perspective many times. In addition to a positive comment from a parent or two, just knowing that I worked with a parent to make a student's year successful can bring its own rewards.

When I was hired for my first teaching position for a multi-age room at a Montessori school, there was some miscommunication. You see, I wasn't trained in the Montessori philosophy but got hired anyway with the understanding that it would be my choice if I wanted to go for more training. At the end of my second year, because I decided not to go for the additional year-long training, the personnel committee and the board president decided that they would not offer me a contract for the next school year. They mistakenly thought I had committed to going for further training.

To my good fortune, when parents heard about my lack of a contract, at least fifteen sets of parents wrote letters to the board, and walked into a personnel committee meeting during the school day to fight for me. Talk about an affirmation of my teaching! I was rehired and stayed at the school for two more years. This situation illustrates what parents will do for an effective teacher. Although some of my teaching methods are unconventional, these parents saw what was going on in the classroom; their children were learning and liked coming to school. That's what parents are looking for.

As Resources

Parents are also invaluable resources for teachers. Many times, parents have added to classroom learning. They have volunteered the use of their county courtroom, helped students meet the State Supreme Court Chief Justice, talked to students about businesses they run, and discussed fundraising for different causes. Other parents have volunteered to bring in large insects for observation from their employer, or demonstrated a specific skill they use at work or in a hobby. Being open to parental involvement is another way to show respect for parents, and the positive outcomes can add much—not only to the classroom, but to me as a teacher and human being.

Here's an example: one parent's dad had fought in World War II, so he volunteered to talk to the class and give his first-hand account of his experience. This grandfather was a soldier who had been on a ship heading to Japan in case the United States had to invade the islands. Because the United States dropped two atomic bombs, he was saved from the danger of the invasion, but he had been to one of the Japanese cities shortly after it had been destroyed. He described to students what it felt like as he stood in the middle of the city; in every direction he looked, nothing was left standing. As he relayed this story, he choked up and had tears in his eyes. It was good for my students to hear this and see how emotional it was to an eighty year old man, sixty years after the event. Students asked tons of questions and went on to hug this courageous man. After his presentation, our class had many discussions on a variety of issues it brought up. This learning experience would never have happened without parental involvement.

In summary, parents are part of the job. Teachers need to find ways to make them partners in the learning process. This usually doesn't just happen, but needs be a conscious effort. In making the effort, teachers become better people and gain untold benefits for the classroom and students.

There are many questions teachers can ask themselves about working with parents. Some of these questions are harder than others to answer, and have been asked by many teachers and administrators. Here are just a few:

1. How can I get parents to share their ideas, careers, and lives with the class to make subjects more real and integrated with other subjects?

2. How am I going to get parent permission slips back?

3. When does something in the room require a call to parents?

4. How do I handle parents bringing in treats?

5. Can I ask them to have treats "student-ready" (pre-cut, and with plates, etc.)?

6. How can they be partners for the year, helping their child?

7. Can I ask parents to be chaperones?

8. How should I communicate my expectations of chaperones?

9. How can I creatively pull parents into the school?

Mumbo Jumbo Summary

In these first six chapters, I've described ways I bring heart into my classroom in a variety of ways: being open to sharing experiences, showing vulnerability as a human being, caring in different ways, being empathetic, designing lessons with students in mind, setting up a warm learning environment, and working with parents. Throughout a school year, these approaches evolve and mature. So do students, and so do I. That's what the classroom is for, and sharing heart and soul will only make that growth more special.

Fun Quotes and Photos

In an airplane for the first time,
ascending above the clouds:
"I think I see God."
Tyrese, 5th Grader

*"I feel like a Beanie Baby,
you're so tall!"*
Rachel, 4th grader

After trying to serve the ball
in volleyball practice,
*"Is there a game where you have to get
the ball under the net instead of over it?!"*
Hailey, 3rd grader

Asked why he was lying on chairs
lined in a row for a game,
"I took advantage of life!"
Ethan, 4th grader

Me: *"What do you want for Christmas?"*
Student: *"A lifetime supply of root beer."*
Aaron, 3rd grader

After asking why he had not gotten to his seat yet
after the direction was given, and
he was merrily jumping around the room,
*"I was in mid-flight of my jump
when you gave the direction."*
Mason, 4th grader

Me: *"What did William Horlick invent? [malted milk]"*
Student: *"If he was bad, asparagus.*
If he was good, sugar!"
Sara, 4th grader

During a trip to Olympic National Park
"I'm going to come out here by myself
so I can do something dangerous."
Cheyenne, 5th grade

PART 2: BANANA PEPPERS

Creative Math Instruction

"How did math start?"

Peter, 4th grader

****

ATTENTION:

Even though this section focuses mainly on math instruction, the ideas translate to other areas of the classroom as well. This section is about engaging students in math lessons and getting them to love coming to math class. However, making math fun and engaging does not mean there are low expectations. On the contrary, my students are expected to try hard, challenge themselves, ask questions, and be honest. One more thing: having high expectations does not mean just more homework for students.

****

Chapter 7

Integration and Differentiation

Connecting language arts
and social studies with math

During a summer program I was running, I asked students to get in line according to certain topics, such as how much they liked broccoli, chocolate ice cream or math. For the question of broccoli, students had the chance to talk about their preferences while getting themselves in line, from loving it to hating it. For the questions of chocolate ice cream and math, they were to use non-verbal communication to get in proper order. Most liked chocolate ice cream, but when students were asked about math, four students immediately jumped to the "hate it" side of the line. They didn't have to think even for a second, or use any hand signals whatsoever, to show their level of disdain for math. As a teacher, it was sad to see, especially when I can get most students to enjoy math. I felt disappointed that I couldn't work with these kids for more than a few weeks. Most likely these students hated math because they considered themselves bad at it or had bad experiences with math while in school.

One of my goals in teaching in general, and in math specifically, is to *not* discourage students, especially at a young age. It seems many math students get discouraged by their performance, the lack of challenge or by a bad teacher. Hearing stories about students who feel discouraged by math drives me to be a better math teacher myself. I may not be 100% successful, but I do knock myself out trying to help all students have a good degree of success in math. I believe much of the discouragement that students feel comes from many teachers not feeling comfortable in their own math skills, and that's too bad. Even if math was not a favorite subject in their childhood, most elementary teachers will have to teach it in their classrooms. Teachers often make a huge difference in the confidence and comfort students have with a subject, but in math great teaching is even more critical. Math teachers can inspire, or discourage. What choice should we make, and what can we do to move all students toward success?

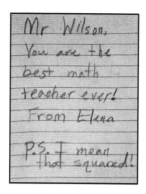

Mr Wilson,
You are the
best math
teacher ever!
From Elena

P.S. I mean
that squared!!

Students learn at different paces. This is an obvious acknowledgment, yet still a tough part of teaching. Learning paces can be different in any subject, but the variety of learning paces in math is one of the biggest challenges for a teacher. With this in mind, I work to make sure all students are exposed to the concepts they need to know, and help all students experience success. I plan my math instruction in a way that all students can gain at least small successes in each lesson. These small successes can be built upon as time goes by.

Knowing not all students will grasp everything instantly is a tough reality to deal with, and I spent years searching for better ways to reach more students. This lack of immediate understanding on the part of students is one of the reasons math tests are used infrequently in my class—I feel testing leads poorer math performers to tell themselves they are bad at math, and this attitude can carry over to the rest of their lives. Why would I do this to nine- and ten-year-olds?

Integrating math instruction with other subjects and activities can help. Integration and added challenges keep students on their toes and gives them something to strive for. Many of the activities I'll be describing involve integration and challenge for students at different levels. This variety within lessons brings concepts together to reach different students' academic and emotional needs.

My most effective lessons are dynamic and multi-layered, planned with forethought, but very flexible. Although planning is a necessary practice, much of the best learning and differentiation in class has flowed from discussions, with minimal planning involved. I visualize and plan my math instruction for the week, month and year, but rarely write lessons more than a few days ahead of time. This lack of over-planning allows for flexibility. Sometimes students learn concepts faster than I expected, sometimes they are slower to catch on. Sometimes, they just need a breather to calm themselves down. Not planning too far ahead forces me to connect instruction to where students are at the moment, and helps me integrate math with other subjects that are being taught in the same time frame. It makes me focus on the present and helps me target student needs. Quite honestly, this method keeps me on edge in a good way. The pressure of keeping things fresh, relevant and challenging gets my creative juices flowing. It also makes my instruction relevant.

While tutoring a third grader on strategies with addition, subtraction and multiplication, our discussion led to a number line moving to the right on the whiteboard. We ended up talking about infinity, which then led to a discussion on negative infinity going the opposite direction. This was something she had never heard of. As we talked about positive and negative numbers, she learned that negative one is the opposite of positive one and when added together they equal zero. This concept was an unplanned detour of our lesson with operations, and it even surprised me that we got to this point. This student came up with the idea of a scale where the sides of the scale would rise, fall or balance depending on the numbers used. She understood this with limited instruction and no plan on my part. The opportunity just presented itself at the very end of our sessions. As her mother picked her up from the room, we shared fist bumps for the progress we made. An hour later, the mother returned with her giggling daughter. The mother said, "I don't know what you do to make her so happy, but she can't stop laughing!" The reason was very simple—her daughter had felt success in math!

Just two days later, I was tutoring a second grader on using a ruler. We discussed how the metric system is used world-wide and how only the United States and limited other countries (i.e. Liberia and Burma) use the Imperial or American system of inches, feet and miles. And we talked about why a country in Africa would use the American system. Was this planned?

No way. Was it a teachable moment? You bet. These are two examples from tutoring, but this kind of activity happens in a full classroom all the time.

Integration of subjects creates more chances for student connections. It also gives struggling math students a chance for success or leadership, since they may have more ability in another subject. An example might be using iPads for a math lesson—maybe a struggling math student is great at iPad apps and can help others during the lesson. This overlap of skills can help their thinking to be more confident while interacting with the math.

Other integrated teachable moments that have popped up within math class include studying geography while recording temperatures of international cities, calculating square footage of Native Americans shelters as we build replicas, learning that teepees are wrapped with semi-circles of material, and cutting mats to frame student-created artwork. The opportunities are unlimited if we are open to serendipitous moments and the creative process involved in learning.

With that said, it doesn't mean I don't differentiate in other ways as well. Teachers most likely will end up trying to reach at least three levels of students: those at grade level, those below level and those at advanced levels. Yes, it is quite a challenge, and it's easier said than done to reach all levels of students. Thinking backwards is where I start. What is my goal for students? How would an adult use this math? What would make students apply concepts in a way that forces them to really know what they're talking about? These are questions I ask myself as I visualize math instruction.

Many times the discussion about reaching different levels will end up being a discussion about grouping versus not grouping. This is an ongoing conversation almost anywhere, and both sides of argument have their points. Grouping by ability advocates might say that grouping gets all students challenged in their zone of proximal development. And I have no argument against that point. But how do we make sure kids in the lowest group don't stay lowest, or psychologically don't peg themselves as bad math students the rest of their lives? And how do we make sure the lowest students get the full extent of the concepts and procedures of their grade level, and not just rote practice work? On the side of no grouping, we end up teaching all students the same concepts simultaneously, but how do we challenge those who already know the concepts and will just get bored to death in a lesson? These are all very pertinent and far-reaching questions. If I really want to teach all students the way I say I do, I have to struggle and challenge myself to solve these questions to the best of my ability.

I've seen successful teachers use various approaches to reach students. Some split students into groups, teaching them at different times of the day, really pushing the more advanced students, meeting the on-level students' needs and somewhat reaching the lower level students' needs. I've also seen this approach leave the lower level students still struggling with their math facts, all the while having them miss a majority of the procedures and concepts that the on-level group experiences. This approach seems to help all but the lower level students, because while they are using their time to practice math facts, they are falling behind on other aspects of their math exposure. How does this help them in the next year? It doesn't—it helps them fall behind even further. That's the problem with having separate ability groups that are set in stone.

In the case of more advanced students, while I am always pushing them to work on challenging contextual problems, I don't want them to be excluded from normal class activities. I want them to stay connected with other students. An added benefit of keeping advanced students with other students is not just that they can help other students, but they can inspire others and provide a positive influence that being good at math can be cool. One year, a new student to the school proved to be well advanced in many aspects of math. As he became friends with some of the boys, his good math ability inspired some of his friends who weren't at the same level to try harder and challenge themselves.

My approach is to basically create a mixture of lessons and approaches. Some days, math is taught with a full group; others are designed with smaller groups. I think this is the most realistic approach for one teacher in a room of 20-30 students. On the days I teach a full group, I target ideas that most students need work with, such as measurement or money. These might be the game days also. This way, all students get to play games and all students are involved together. On the days when I split students into groups, I have focused small-group lessons for those who need it, while the other students work on projects (like Boxes, explained in the next chapter), read or practice skills in productive ways. Students not in the small-group lesson are *not* just given worksheets to work on all of the time. They are most often given a more focused goal while I work with other students. This approach does take juggling on the teacher's part to keep things straight and make sure all students are on task and challenged at their level, but it's well worth it. And it's had great results for students.

Someone might be saying, "These are all fine and dandy ideas, but how do I really do it?" Teachers want to reach all levels of students, but the "how" is the tough part. This is *exactly* why I teach math the way I do. In the following chapters, I'll explain my methods and the thinking behind them.

> After a student learned how to
> make equivalent fractions,
> she passionately proclaimed:
> *"Math is really an art!"*
> Elena, 4th grader

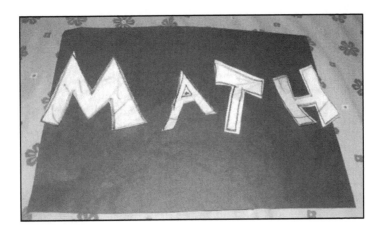

Chapter 8

Boxes

"This box could stop a war."
Isabella, 4th grader

"Mr. Wilson, are we working on boxes today?" This is a common question in my fourth grade classroom. Although it might not sound interesting, it's pretty cool to see students getting excited about school work, especially about something as plain as a box. Fourth grade boxes have become something special.

At the beginning of the year, students are asked to bring in consumer boxes from things their families have bought. Over the course of a few days, students bring boxes of all shapes and sizes into school. Parents do as well. And what we see is amazing. In class, we see boxes for wine, sporting goods, electronics, chocolate, soaps, spices and much more. Throughout the year, students occasionally surprise the rest of us by bringing in even more complex boxes they've found; boxes for Star Wars light sabers, Legos and volleyballs have been very interesting.

We start math class having students open boxes they've brought in and slowly disassemble them. As we discuss how the boxes came into existence, students learn that they were designed flat and they were created by someone who knew math. They pay close attention to how they were made, because most consumer boxes are made with one piece of paper cut into crazy patterns. Some boxes may have flaps that fold into each other, while others have glue to hold them together. Other boxes have specially designed holes, pull tabs or sections for hanging the product in stores. Students are amazed and engaged in the discussion, and start to notice certain aspects, like tabs used to glue one side to another or notches to hold other tabs.

The box project began when I realized the power of looking at everyday consumer boxes that were created flat. In mathematical terms, these flat designs are called "nets." Students have no idea just how much math is involved in the design and manufacture of boxes, until they take a look. Then the curiosity begins!

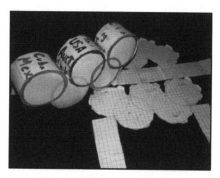

Box designed by Gloria T.

In math classes around the country, most instruction is guided by textbooks and standards. That's not necessarily a bad thing. And within this instruction, geometry and problem-solving skills are topics teachers work on with students. Sometimes these topics are taught in specific units, while at other times they are addressed in smaller sections spread out through the school year. But working through units or acing tests on topics does not mean students are masters of them. Because of this, many hands-on approaches are used to help students master the ideas of polygons, line and angle measurement, visual-spatial relationships, area, volume and perimeter. To be proficient with these topics, students need to use the skills and knowledge they are acquiring in deep, meaningful ways. That is where boxes come in within my fourth grade classroom.

Designing boxes created from one large, flat piece of paper is how my students make incredible gains in these areas. When the idea came to me to use boxes in class, I had no idea it would turn into the coolest, most challenging, and most creative project in my fourth grade math instruction. Usually, the crazy ideas I use within math lessons make it fun and unique, but this box project has created a problem-solving and design element of the classroom that is truly inspiring.

To start their own boxes, students learn how a cube is designed from a flat "net," and then they go from there. They make their own cubes from grid paper, noticing that a cube is really just six square sides arranged so that they fold together to form the 3D object.

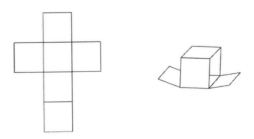

After starting with cubes, students move on to create pyramids and triangular prisms. As they work with these shapes, they notice that a four-sided pyramid is really just a square with a triangle coming off each side folded up to connect to each other.

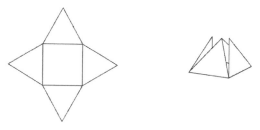

A triangular prism is just three rectangles connected together with one equilateral triangle at each end of one rectangle.

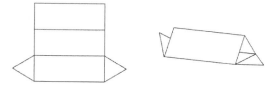

Once these shapes are mastered, the creativity really kicks in. Each new design must be more complicated, and the complexity students have come up with stuns me and most observers. Their creative ideas have included hexagonal prisms, pentagonal dodecahedrons (twelve-sided pentagons), hearts, wedding cakes, dogs, tea pots, butterflies, robots, skyscrapers, and even Olympic rings. All designs require different thinking and precision in their creation, and all take "math class" and put it into kids' hands, instead of in a notebook. For instance, the dodecahedron shown below is made up of twelve pentagons. Within each of those pentagons are five angles of 108 degrees. In addition to the angles, all of the sides need to measure the same length (i.e. 4 cm). As you can imagine, a student will become a master of a protractor after drawing the sixty angles needed for the entire design!

Box designed by Hailey B.

The boxes give kids of many different abilities the chance to be challenged and successful in their own unique ways. Therefore, it's a great way to differentiate instruction and create challenge. More advanced math students choose extremely complicated designs, and they run into challenges they have to learn to work through. This is something they may not be used to doing. Many students who are good at math have things come to them very easily, and when they don't "get" something right away, it somewhat freaks them out. It's as if the struggle of learning is so new for them that they may want to stop. They, too, have to learn to get through the feeling of not being successful immediately. In one instance, a student with excellent math sense was working on an extremely advanced concept for a box. When presented with new concepts or procedures during our more structured instruction time, he was used to immediately grasping the ideas. To create his new design though, he had to use a protractor to measure angles, which was new to him. I could see the challenge written on his face and hear it in his remarks. He got a bit frustrated and had to fight through it. He kept at the use of a protractor in the design of his box and he became a master.

There are examples of students at the other end of the spectrum as well—those who might struggle with their math skills. Some students need extra help with measurement using a ruler or protractor, or in seeing the visual-spatial aspect of a box. After working on less complicated designs in the box project, these students have gone on to work on hexagonal prisms, spheres, "T" boxes, or even turtles.

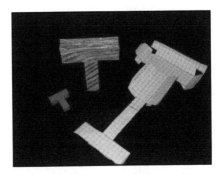

Another student who struggled with drawing or cutting straight lines made a special connection between subjects. As students were working on learning latitude and longitude in social studies, we started with the story of John Harrison, who invented the chronometer to solve the longitude navigation problem. After practicing latitude and longitude using spheres and hemispheres, we began work with two-dimensional world maps. As students looked at different maps, they learned about the variety of projections cartographers have created to show a spherical shape on a flat piece of paper. One in particular stood out to this student—the view where the globe is split into equal, conical shapes connected at the equator, with each point bending over to meet at the poles to create a folded spherical shape.

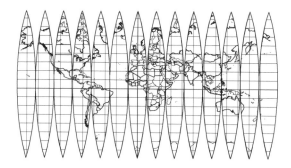

After finishing a box with a partner, this student approached me to ask if she could create a box that was based on this global projection. With my support, she went on to create the spherical box shown below. As she progressed through the year, this student kept pushing herself with even more creative designs and her problem-solving growth was tremendous. Her sense of self-worth improved as well, as she created even more complicated boxes. Her progress was a testament to her courage and determination as a ten-year-old. As you can see, the box project has the potential to reach all students, no matter the level. Students may make progress at different paces, but all get to practice their skills using a protractor, a ruler, the idea of symmetry, and the concept of thinking in 2D and 3D.

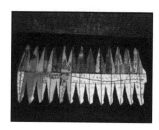

Another student started out the year having trouble figuring out where lines should go and how to count the right amount of boxes on the graph paper. She needed consistent support through each new design. As we wound down the box project during the last week of school, we had about twenty minutes left to finish a box, so I asked her to come up with something fast. And did she! With no help from me, she created a rectangular prism with windows that would have taken her several days with support earlier in the year. She learned how to measure and visualize, and it was thrilling to see her perseverance and growth.

The box project has expanded in other ways as well. One student's parents own a spice company, so the mother brought in many boxes, including flat templates that weren't folded, to show students just how their company's boxes are made. Another example was when a student was looking in an interactive book about oceanology and saw a removable box in one of its sleeves. She came running to me, "Look Mr. Wilson, a box!" This same girl also connected our study of architecture to boxes as she pointed out her next box design from a book on skyscrapers. Others have connected area and space design to childrens' books which show side and bird's eye views of different rooms. These types of reactions and class connections become more commonplace throughout the school year. Two students even created a box based on a consumer box that had a window in front and extra tabs to hold light bulbs.

I suggested they make it a box for "Qbert," the class buffalo, and design it as if it would be hung in a toy store.

Box designed by Camille R. and Emmett M.

People are always telling us to think outside the box. This project asks us to look *at* the box. This idea didn't come to me while reading through textbooks or sitting in on a professional development session. I wasn't striving to find a math project. It came to me as I went through my normal day, and my mind subconsciously went about its business. As it turns out, students have made this project much more than I ever could have. It has opened up student perceptions of things around them, and it's been incredible to watch students as they create. And it all started with a box! The point here is this: find ideas that kids can get excited about. These types of ideas are all around us; we just have to be available to see them.

One last thing: a teacher from across the hallway brought me a copy of her son's homework from the previous night. It included a problem that reminded her of the box project. The problem in the homework involved looking at a shape and finding which "net," or flat piece of paper, was folded to create the 3D shape. During math class that day, I wrote the problem on the board and asked students to work on it for a few minutes in small groups. I explained where the problem came from, but didn't tell students which grade that teacher's son was in. After a few minutes, every group chose the correct answer from the multiple-choice options. I then told them the problem was from a tenth grade math textbook. That blew the kids away. Me, too.

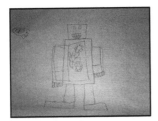 

Box designed by Teddi P.

Chapter 9

Connecting Math with the "Real World"

During a lesson on an upcoming business unit,
*"If we're supposed to be running our business unit
so realistically, how come we can't use calculators?"*
Audrey, 4th grader

On a Sunday during one school year, my girlfriend Kim and I happened to visit Windpoint Lighthouse on the shores of Lake Michigan in Racine, Wisconsin. We both were enjoying a beautiful fall day next to the lake and wandered into an old foghorn building that had been turned into a museum. I shared what happened next with my students the following day. I wanted them to see that math happens in the least expected places. And that even math teachers can be confused if they aren't present in the moment.

As I perused miscellaneous items within the museum, I noticed a small fragment of information taped to a glass box enclosing a model ship. The information explained the average depth of the lake was about 290 feet, while the maximum depth was about 970 feet. When I looked at the adjacent wall, there was a visual of the lake showing contour lines of depths labeled between 50 and 250. These contour lines are called bathymetric contours. As I scanned for something close to 900, my mind played tricks on me. Was the 970-foot depth of the lake so small it wouldn't show up on a bathymetry? Had the water gone down so much that the contours were out of date? I *knew* those weren't correct answers flowing through my mind, but I was so lost in other thoughts that I didn't grasp the obviousness of the mix-up. Kim looked at the difference and immediately pointed out that the bathymetric contours were in a scale using meters. Wow, no kidding!

In class the next day, I discussed the event with my students, projecting two similar items on the Smartboard. I shared this story with students for many reasons—to show them that math is always around us, to show them the difference between meters and feet, but most importantly to show them that adults, even math teachers, make mistakes. There was nothing wrong with me for making a mistake. It was a natural occurrence, but it was also something I could correct without feeling ashamed. Did I feel a bit embarrassed in front of Kim when it happened? Just slightly. Did I feel embarrassed to share this story with my students? Not one bit.

Finding a radius

Although some people may not like the idea, we have to admit numbers and their uses are everywhere. With this reality in mind, I bring worldly math into the classroom every chance I get. By integrating real-life math situations into the classroom, all students get to realize just how important math is in our lives— and they get to use math in ways that are pertinent. I ask students to look for math or numbers wherever they may be, and they learn to find them in the least expected spots: a company named ME^2, hiking boots with a "45" on their sides, or a latitude/longitude sign in front of a house. Math and numbers are everywhere. Instead of resisting the reality, I want students to have an attitude of curiosity about it.

My fourth grade class visited a dairy farm this past spring, where I was naively surprised to find out just how much math is involved in the process, from keeping cows separated by age to tracking how much they eat, how much milk they produce, the percent of ingredients in feed, or how many steps they take measured with pedometers on their ankles. The statistics the farm used to run their business were impressive. Other examples I have used that show math in the real world are: using the oil slick in the Gulf of Mexico a few years ago to help students understand surface area, an Empire carpet commercial helping students learn about percentages off of a price, or discussing the depths of hotel pools showing both metric and standard units.

As teachers, we need to think about all the things outside a classroom that can be made into real-life math problems or real-world situations that can be brought into the classroom. What makes sense and is doable? I bet a lot more than we initially might think. When we bring real-world examples into the classroom, students can see the importance of symmetry, the tenths place value or using a protractor, just to name a few math concepts. Work in the classroom can then be adjusted to encompass examples from outside the classroom.

Shape of a Hotel

Hotel Pool Depths

Buying Door Handles

The doors of a cabinet in my classroom needed new handles, each requiring two holes to tighten the handles to the door. I wanted to fix this cabinet problem as I prepared for the new school year, so I carefully measured the distance between the holes, an important part of finding the right handles. I used a standard ruler as accurately as possible, and my measurement was between $3\,^3/_4$ inches and $3\,^7/_8$ inches. I found this curious but didn't think to use the metric side of the ruler.

After driving to a local Home Depot, an employee ushered me to the correct aisle to peruse the different handles. As I scanned the wall of handles, many styles were available with their between-hole dimensions displayed prominently. On the middle of the wall was a graphic showing common distances between handle holes, those that the store carried. All of the standard sizes were on the graphic, but there was no standard measurement listed between $3\,^1/_2$ inches and 4 inches. There was a 96 mm graphic though. The employee and I both got into a quandary looking at the graphic because, while looking at the actual drawers for handles, we found some that were labeled $3\,^3/_4$ inches. I decided one of those must be close to what I was looking for, so I pulled a packaged handle from a drawer. The label of the package didn't read $3\,^3/_4$ inches, but 96 mm. This was very odd since the label on the drawer posted the distance in inches, yet the handle was in millimeters. As we talked, the sales clerk mentioned that she had learned something that day, and so had I. I also got the handles I was looking for, and had yet another example to show students.

If I would have required the students to find out which handle to buy, would they have known that the measurement between holes was important? Most probably would never have thought of that requirement, even though they would have visually been able to see it. This type of example shows them these everyday uses of math and gives us a way to use measurement in class in a real way.

Mocha!

I never thought I'd be much of a coffee drinker, but have become quite the mocha drinker. I've gone from stopping by a local establishment once a month to the cashiers knowing my order when I walk in the door. Yes, I've come a long way, and I bet many readers have had the same thing happen! As I paid for my mocha and a sweet roll one day, my loyalty card registered a credit balance of $14.50, and the total of my new order was $4.51. In my head, I immediately knew my new balance would be $9.99.

How did I know the new balance so quickly in my head? These are the type of things I bring into the classroom. There are math skills we use in the real world all of the time that need to be taught explicitly for students to connect their classroom learning to life outside the room. In this case, some students would think they had to go through the entire subtraction procedure, because that's the way they have been taught. I want my students to understand math and how we can use it better than that. Yes, I want them to know procedures, but, even more, I want them to be able to use math as citizens in the real world. This awareness could also be carried over into math inside the classroom. From this example, I may design a decimal number lesson that involves money and change at a restaurant, or use of store gift cards.

Cards

A report about a casino said a gambler won an outlandish amount of money, and the casino accused him of cheating. The article caught my attention because of the math concept that was involved—symmetry and asymmetry. You see, this casino's cards had a diamond pattern, and the gambler noticed that some of the cards were cut incorrectly so that just a bit of a diamond showed on one edge. He basically noticed that some of the cards were now asymmetrical, and therefore would stand out from others. He used this knowledge to gain an advantage in his betting on the card game. The casino caught on and didn't take it very well. Here's an example of symmetry mattering in the real world that students can understand. From here, I may design a lesson in which students draw their own symmetrical card designs.

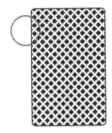 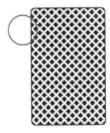

Cold Weather!

Learning about positive and negative numbers isn't too hard in Wisconsin because of our crazy, long winters. But one day stood out last year; my sister was 100 degrees warmer than I was! She was in the U. S. Virgin Islands, where it was 80 degrees, while it was -20 in Wisconsin and we had "cold days" away from school. Thinking about someone being 100 degrees warmer was nuts, and students were amazed! In that particular school year, four days of school were cancelled because of extreme cold. It's easy to see how this example could be used to help students learn positive and negative numbers. A discussion on absolute value may follow to explain that all numbers are a certain distance from zero. It's a simple idea, but by using an interesting scenario, it becomes engaging and meaningful.

Restaurants

While walking into a restaurant, the sign announcing its specials caught my eye. It read "$7.9." I wondered if they made a mistake by not adding a "0" in the hundredths place value to make it read

"$7.90." Once seated and looking at the menu, I realized they didn't make a mistake; every item on the menu was listed with only the dollars and tenths of a dollar. This layout must have been a design element, or the owners just thought using the extra zero in the hundredths place value was a waste of time or ink. It reminds me of what people may think of certain letters in words now that texting on phones has become so prevalent. Some may think all the vowels in words are unnecessary. In the case of the extra zero in the hundredths place, it's not necessarily required, but it was still an odd occurrence to see. I brought this example into the classroom, because my students need to understand that $7.9 = $7.90. I've seen it since at the McDonald's drive-thru also.

These decimal place value examples are used to make sure that students really know their place values. Do they know that $7.9 does not equal $7.09? I want to make sure and show them how it makes a difference in the real world.

Television or Web Videos

With the amount of television and Internet in our students' lives, the amount of math involved in both mediums would take a lifetime to demonstrate. Every day, something interesting could be shared. Here are just a few examples we've discussed in class.

A year ago, a video of a husband and wife in a car went viral. In the video, while driving and recording the conversation, the husband asked his wife, "If you're traveling 80 mph, how far will you travel in one hour?" Since the video went viral, you can imagine the wife's response was not eighty miles. She over-thought the problem and started throwing out a variety of irrelevant factors into her thought process.

As I showed the video to my students, some understood the "bad math" that was demonstrated, but many did not see the obvious answer. These students had heard about miles per hour, but most were unable to use the concept. It was still a nebulous term they never had to utilize. It was just some idea in math problems or just a term their parents threw around occasionally. The point in showing the video was that I didn't want my students to be that kind of adult—an adult that let a math situation become a national comedy! I wanted them to realize the math concepts we talk about in class are used in life. And they didn't need to let the concepts confuse them, when most are actually very logical. Using this example, we had a chance to discuss what miles per hour really meant and then were able to practice examples in class.

My students find out pretty quickly that I'm a fan of the Jeopardy game show. I watch the show every weekday, and every once in a while the show has a math category. It's interesting to see if the contestants shy away from the category or not—most of the time, they do. If I catch it quickly enough, I take screen shots of the clues to bring into class the next day.

Races

The examples of numbers used in races is unlimited, be it speed skating, horses or Indy cars. Each year, three-year-old thoroughbreds run the Triple Crown races: the Kentucky Derby, the Preakness, and the Belmont Stakes. I've always loved watching these races with my mom, grandmother and sister. Each race is a different length, using fractions: $1 \frac{1}{4}$ mile, $1 \frac{3}{16}$ mile, $1 \frac{1}{2}$ mile respectively. During the Triple Crown stretch of one spring semester, "I'll Have Another" and "Bodemeister" battled in the first two races. Before being scratched from the Belmont Stakes, "I'll Have Another" had a chance to win the Triple Crown. In class, we watched replays of both the Derby and the Preakness because both races were close. Kids weren't told which horse won, but were able to pick their horse and then cheer as we watched. Watching the races ended up being very exciting, and kids learned to use fractions in a new way, because of the lengths of the races. Instead of just writing fractions on paper and talking about common denominators or equivalency, students were able to draw and discuss the lengths of the races and why they mattered to the horses' owners.

Another race on television was even closer than the horse races. As I surfed the web one day, I ended up watching the end of the 2013 Firestone Freedom 100. (I would recommend watching this race on YouTube to anyone who likes competition.) The video was shown to students with a bit of an introduction, telling them how infrequently a three-wide race happens in Indy car racing. Without telling students the outcome, I let them choose a car to cheer for. As the race plays out, and the announcers excitedly describe the cars racing toward the checkered flag, a fourth car comes out of nowhere to win the race. The race was won by 0.0026 of a second. In his excitement, one of the announcers made a mistake and translated that number to twenty-six one-thousandths of a second. But a moment later, he corrected himself, saying it was twenty-six ten-thousandths of a second. Not only was the race exciting to watch, but the math involved took the study of decimal numbers to a new level.

One more example of the importance of decimal place values happened in the 2014 Winter Olympics 1500M Men's Speed Skating finals. The results of the race showed both skaters had clocked the exact same time (1:45:00). The times displayed to the television and stadium audiences were to the hundredths of a second, but the official race results were timed to the nearest thousandth of second. Using the official timing, the Polish skater beat the other skater by 0.003 of a second (1:45:006 to 1:45:009) to win the gold medal. As we talked about the race in class, students were asked if they thought the thousandths place value mattered to these racers. You can bet they exclaimed, "Yes!"

These examples of numbers in real life are great teaching moments for students. This racing example could easily be transferred into a fun class experiment, seeing which student could count by tens the fastest to one hundred or say the alphabet the fastest. An Internet stop watch can easily be found to time each student.

Concepts students learn in class do make a difference in people's lives. One final example is an excellent demonstration of this. On a newscast about wakeboarding, a video displayed a wakeboarder high above the water level. The reporter mentioned that a wakeboarder could reach up to nine feet above the water, but it was obvious that the height of the wakeboarder in the video was much greater than nine feet. A few seconds later, the reporter corrected herself to say nine meters. The difference between nine meters and nine feet is very large—nine meters is about twenty-nine and half feet. As in the video about the speed skaters, I asked my students if this might make a difference to someone who was new to the sport and a bit tentative about the heights that could be achieved. You can imagine their agreement.

The reason students learn math is to be knowledgeable adults who are able to function in our society. While some of the math concepts used in advanced classes won't be used by all students when they become adults, there are many aspects of math we use almost every day. Whether it's miles per hour, decimal numbers used in monetary transactions or the fractional measuring used in a recipe, math concepts need to be transferred from "book" learning to real situations. Bringing in examples from our society gives students the opportunity to practice the skills they'll need the rest of their lives.

Chapter 10

Understanding Student Thinking and Using Explicit Instruction

"Three is faster than zero, because three has only one syllable and zero has two."
Alexa, 4th grader

Students give us hints into their thinking all the time. Do we listen? And I mean really listen? Sometimes it's very easy for teachers to act like we're listening when we really just have our own agenda in mind. Sometimes the day just seems too rushed to hear everything students have to offer or ask, and that is a shame. In our society today, it seems everyone is in a time-crunch. But then a student asks a fantastic question, and it stops us in our tracks and makes us realize there's more to learning than getting through everything. If we aren't listening well enough, we need a wakeup call to change our rushed schedule or our response to students. In math instruction, this can be extremely important.

One thing I do every so often is to take a class period to intentionally stop and take a "breather," to listen and clarify. The first time I did this, I wondered if there'd be enough questions to fill a lesson period and keep everyone's attention. It's easy to feel insecure going into an open discussion with kids, not knowing if anyone will share. Going in, I made sure to have a lesson ready in case the discussion totally bombed and we were sitting there wasting time, but it didn't happen that way.

Kids seemed thrilled to take a breather and have the opportunity to ask questions. It seemed like they had never had the chance to do it either, to just catch up and smooth out some of their confusions or doubts. They asked a variety of questions, things I never would have considered. Some had trouble verbalizing their questions, but they still craved clarification. And they wanted to be involved; they weren't just sitting there hoping to be invisible and watching the clock. They genuinely wanted to get things clarified for themselves.

For example, I've found almost all students, even those with advanced math ability, need explicit instruction on how to decipher word problems, especially multi-step ones. Many students show good progress in procedures, but have a bit of a struggle when trying to apply them in word problems. This is a spot where a full-group session can be useful, where students can share their perception of what a word problem is asking, and clarify what needs to be done. In full-group sessions on word problems, students are taught to look for numbers that are useful in answering the question, and also for those numbers that are unusable. I make the analogy of those games where a coin is dropped into a panel with obstacles that alter its path; the coin can end up in several different spots at the bottom.

Students are guided to use their brains to filter information and use procedures to get that coin into the correct spot at the bottom of the game. This is just one strategy that can be used in a full group with different numbers for different levels of math ability, if necessary.

While this strategy can be used to solve problems, it may not always get to the root mathematical reasoning that students need to master. This is why multiple approaches always need to be used and taught explicitly. During our discussions with students, we often will tell them their questions are our priority, but in reality we don't take nearly enough time to answer these questions. And students learn not to ask. To counter this, we need to set up interactions so they can ask. The rest of this chapter is dedicated to examples of listening to students and observing them in a real class.

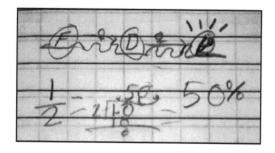

While teaching a student how to change
fractions to decimals to percents,
she drew hills between F...D....P saying:
"Numbers are going over mountains
to become percents in the land of paradise."
Elena, 4th grader

When counting sixteenths of an inch on a ruler, many kids learn to look at just a specific length mark on the ruler to tell them what fraction of an inch a certain distance is. This is logical, since the different lengths ($^1/_{16}$, $^1/_8$, $^1/_4$, $^1/_2$) on a ruler are designed to make recognizing them easier. But many students don't quite get the logic that the marks are measuring out distances between marks, not just one spot on the ruler. For instance, if students count only the visible $^1/_{16}$ marks from the end of a ruler, they'll count $^3/_{16}$ as $^2/_{16}$ because they will see only two of that length marks from the end of the ruler (a $^1/_8$ mark is in between them). If this isn't explained, understood and practiced, many kids go on making mistakes with rulers.

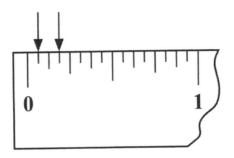

This is a prime example of the basic theme of this chapter—very intentional instruction and discernment of student thinking. There are many intricate details and levels of instruction that delve into students' thinking that teachers need to pay attention to for students to truly reach exceptional learning in the classroom.

Before I was a teacher, a German student visited the company where I worked. Several colleagues and I took him to a Milwaukee Brewers baseball game and then attempted to teach him the rules of the game. It took about an hour, and we didn't come close to explaining everything. To us, as Americans growing up in the 1960s and '70s, baseball was an easy game to understand. To my German friend, the depth of each aspect of the game made it more complicated as we went along; balls, strikes, foul balls, tagging up, force outs, and grand slams were just too much to absorb in one sitting. His questions as we went along gave us an insight into what he was thinking: Why does a foul ball on a third strike not count as a strikeout? What does over-running a base mean? What is a "trap"? These questions led our teaching and got us deeper into baseball.

This story reminds me of students in the classroom learning the basics of mathematics, or other subjects, as the concepts and procedures keep building on each other. It's a teacher's crazy job to keep getting deeper, but this can overwhelm students. To be a great teacher includes trying to think as kids might as you plan lessons, paying close attention to students' comments during lessons and then reflecting about the lessons afterward.

Each of us sees numbers in our own unique way, and although we as teachers may think we have the best way of seeing a problem, there are plenty of alternative ways to view numbers. While working with a third-grader on multiplication facts, I could see she didn't know the facts automatically, but was using some mental strategy to think about the numbers. We stopped and had a conversation so she could tell me what she was doing in her mind. She was manipulating numbers in a way I had never seen before. We talked about how there are many strategies to solving problems and that as long as she got correct answers her strategy would work. But I also mentioned that as she got older and math became more complex she might need to use different strategies to speed things up and use her mind for more complicated processes. She got that. And by the time our tutoring hour ended she was working on three-digit by two-digit multiplication for the first time ever. When her mother picked her up, she said, "It's fun!" The point is, we spent time talking about her thinking. Even in a full group setting, these short conversations with students can go a long way in letting all students know they can see things differently and not be unusual. The conversations also help us discern where students are in their thinking.

A teacher's discernment is very important. It's important to concentrate on what students are saying, but also on what they aren't saying by paying attention to their inflections and facial expressions. I sometimes push or pry a bit by asking if they really get it or are just saying so. It's actually pretty easy to tell. And if they don't get something, I ask them to tell me what they're thinking at that point in time. Even this might be a challenge for them. This approach might seem obvious, but if we don't make a point of working this way, many teachable moments disappear without being taken advantage of.

> *"I thought parallel was only for horizontal lines."*
> Ricky, 4th grader

As students move through the school year, hundreds of questions and answers will be shared between all of us in the classroom. These questions and answers will come from a variety of angles; some will make a lot of sense, and some will come from left field. These student questions and answers contain vital information for a teacher. We want them to ask, so we need to make sure it's safe for them to do so.

After being in a classroom with elementary students, it still amazes me the different ways students may understand or view a problem. Some students who are amazing at math may see things from such a complex, forward-thinking view that sometimes I can't see what they mean. Other students who may not be as amazing at math can also see problems in varied, valid ways.

Valid is the key term here because teachers need to respect students' perspectives. It's also our job to make sure students don't laugh at new and surprising views on numbers or ways to manipulate numbers that other students suggest. In one class, one student had some of the most refreshing ways of seeing math problems. I often had to stop and have the student repeat what he said to smooth out my own confusion on his perspective— even the teacher got confused. But once he explained what he was thinking more thoroughly, it actually made sense. This episode also helped my relationship with this student, gave him great acknowledgment of his own thinking and boosted his self-confidence.

In another class, we were discussing changing a mixed number to an improper fraction (i.e. $3\,{}^1/_2 = {}^7/_2$). I wrote $3\,{}^1/_2$ down on the board and broke the whole number 3 into ${}^2/_2 + {}^2/_2 + {}^2/_2$ and then added the other ${}^1/_2$. Students were then asked how many halves the sum would equal; they answered either four or seven. Seven made sense to me, four did not. When asked about the answer of four, a student explained that she saw four sets of halves, which in her own perception wasn't wrong. Although not mathematically correct, I could see how she got her answer, so I acknowledged that and then clarified things for her. This is the type of occurrence that can happen daily. A difference in perception can make a huge difference in a student's mind. If a perception is made a negative, that student might feel like the viewpoint was incorrect.

We have to be secure enough in our own understanding of math to be okay with a student seeing something in a different way. There may be as many views as there are students in the classroom. While we may not be able to listen to each and every view all the time, making an effort to see these views can open up understandings for many students. Some teachers come into the subject of math thinking they must show the students they know more than they really do, out of insecurity. New or different views might intimidate an insecure teacher, which may create an environment where students' questions are not acknowledged or validated. We can't let insecurity about our teaching keep us from being real. Students will respect a teacher that allows students to have different views and understandings. A teacher who is real and will listen to students is a positive influence for all students. Students notice validation of ideas or perceptions.

Using Strategies

Students are amazing with their insights and abilities for solving problems; they seem to be able to create strategies for themselves without realizing they use them or without verbalizing them. At other times students can surprise us the other way, with their lack of understanding or confidence. A concept we think is obvious or implied might not be so obvious.

In a few cases, I've discerned students' thinking that was unrealistic—they thought "good" students didn't need to use strategies. In math, quirky strategies are used all the time. Struggling students may not be thinking about strategies because they have no idea even good students, or the adult teacher, use them. In actuality, "good" students are using strategies all the time, they just aren't announcing them or aren't conscious of them. Struggling students don't seem to have these same innate mental strategies, so they must be taught them explicitly. Strategies need to be exposed so all students can use them.

> While working with fractional parts of a whole:
> Me: "If $1/3$ of the tank is filled,
> how much is unfilled?"
> Student: "The rest"
> Chloe, 5th grader

One time, a student and I were working on an addition problem of "8 + 5 = ?" I could tell the student was counting up from 8 in her head. She got the right answer, but it took a long time, plus she could have easily made an error. I showed her what I do in my head without really even thinking about it. I find what number can be added to eight to make it a ten, and then add the difference between that number and the second number being added. In this example, I make it 8 + 2 = 10, find 5 − 2 = 3, then add 3 to 10 to get thirteen. She had never thought about numbers that way. This strategy might seem obvious and may have been taught to her earlier in her life, but she wasn't using it. After practicing with this strategy, her speed and accuracy improved and she loved it. She had success, which is a key, even if it's small.

Often times even small things we do as adults don't come naturally to students, like making small drawings or diagrams for ourselves to help with numbers in a problem. Whether it's a math word problem, or some real-world situation like cutting mats for photos, I draw out or jot numbers down as I work through problems. Many students don't want to go through the bother or think they should be able to solve problems without strategies. I make sure they not only think about making diagrams or acronyms (such as PEMDAS for order of operations), but that they actually use them. I stress to students that using some way to organize numbers for themselves is a great strategy—shoot, even their teachers need to use strategies. Students need to be told these things explicitly.

I am a very good speller, but still need to say to myself, "E – A – U" to remember the correct spelling of "beautiful." This example is about spelling, but I've included it because sometimes we use strategies that might not even be considered "math" strategies to solve math problems. A reading strategy used in math is a good example. Try this problem: Rick sold three toys for $.25 each. His customer gave him $1 to pay for the toys. How much change should Rick give back to his customer?

When students were given this problem, they gave either $.25 or $.75 as their answer. Some students thought the customer only bought one product, so they answered $.75. We talked about inference in math problems, because I had written the problem meaning he had bought multiple "toy$\underline{s}$" from Rick, which would produce an answer of $.25 in change. This example illustrates two concepts: one, math strategies take many forms, and two, a math problem can be written too vaguely.

While working with another student, we came across another vague word problem. It asked how much gas was used on a car trip if the tank held 0.05 of its capacity after the trip. Nowhere in the problem did it say the trip started with a full tank of gas, but it was implied since a rental car was used. Would students know this? Maybe or maybe not, but it was a poorly written problem that needed some inferencing to solve it.

"What if you did a PEMDAS [order of operations]
problem with infinity?"
Leah, 4th grader

More Perspectives

When teaching students about reciprocals, I used fractions such as $^3/_2 \times {}^2/_3 = {}^6/_6 = 1$, $^4/_3 \times {}^3/_4 = {}^{12}/_{12} = 1$, or $^7/_8 \times {}^8/_7 = {}^{56}/_{56} = 1$. One of the students picked up on the pattern and asked if reciprocals always had numerators and denominators that were only one digit apart. I never even thought about that as I wrote the problem. But I do now. In another example using reciprocals, mixed numbers and improper fractions were added to the mix. As we worked through the process, one student changed $2\,\frac{1}{2}$ to $2\,\frac{2}{1}$ thinking she only had to take the reciprocal of the fractional part of the mixed number and not think about the whole number. Both of these examples gave me a chance to further clarify unexpected issues that I obviously hadn't thoroughly explained. As you can see, student learning can improve tremendously if we give them the chance to talk and ask questions.

No Extend Page

In a class of young minds, students' habits or perceptions can be very funny. Many students like to start problems wherever they want to on a notebook page, without thinking they may need room below to solve it. When I asked a classroom of students why this happens, some thought it was because kids didn't think ahead, while others made up silly reasons. We laughed about students writing long division problems on the bottom of their pages, giving themselves no room to figure them out. Other students might write problems too close to the right side of the page, thus running out of room on the page for the answers. A logical method of writing problems on a page is for students to give themselves enough room under or next to their problems to actually do the calculations. Because of this, I had to make some students aware that they should think ahead before writing problems on paper, to give themselves more room to work. We made light of this while working on the Smartboard doing problems together.

If a problem gets too long on a Smartboard, there is an "extend page" button that provides more room to work. As a class, we joked about notebooks not having an "extend page" on them, so students should start their problems higher on a page. The inside joke became our end-of-the-year mantra, and it worked. At least, I thought it did. Even with these lessons on awareness, one boy announced that he ran out of space on his page. When we looked at his page, the problem was written at the bottom of the page, with about five inches of blank lines above the problem. When asked why he did it that way, he said, "It was just too hard for my hand to reach up to the middle of the page!" Yeah, right!

"Extending" a division problem

More Page Ideas

Often, tactics that adults use are so obvious that we don't think to tell students about them. When measuring and then cutting out specific sized rectangles from a regular piece of paper, it makes sense to an adult to use the already straight and perpendicular sides of a piece of paper to use as two of the sides. This simplifies the process to just measuring and cutting two straight sides to form a rectangle.

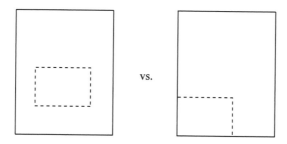

Many students would start by drawing a rectangle in the middle of a page. This is why explicit instructions on even simple tasks can get students to understand how to think logically as they problem-solve.

Another example will prove the point further. Usually, when students are learning to use a protractor, angles that are given to them to measure have the bottom ray of the angle shown parallel to the bottom of the page of a book or worksheet, as shown below. But what do they do when an angle is drawn differently as shown in the second example? Some don't think to either rotate the page or rotate the protractor to make it easier to measure.

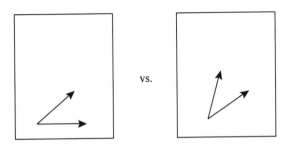

Using a protractor to measure an angle involves more than we might imagine. In this case, we can't limit our teaching to just showing them how to measure an angle that is parallel to bottom of a page or opens up to the right. What if an angle opens up to the left? Do they then think the angle is 150 degrees, using the wrong number on the protractor? If we want to make sure students can solve problems of various complexities, we must have our students gain more than just a limited understanding of concepts and ideas.

Sense-making

Sense-making is an area that constantly needs to be taught explicitly, especially in math. Here's a typical problem: 1,418 divided by 7.

$$7\overline{)1,418}$$

The answer is 202 with a remainder of 4. Some students will come up with an answer of 22 with a remainder of 4 because they won't realize they need to put a zero in the tens place value in their quotient (the answer) while working through the process. When students are first introduced to the long division algorithm (and its connection to multiplication), many struggle to know what the answer means. Even using the long division bracket can be confusing, since the divisor is the number to the left of the bracket; students may read the problem backwards, as 7 divided by 1,418. And learning the definitions of divisor, dividend or quotient is not always easy. In this type of problem, the first step students learn procedurally is to divide 14 by 7 and then put a 2 above the 4 on top of the line (in the hundred's place value). But even if students are aware of this, many students have no idea what the numbers on top of the bracket really mean. Putting the above problem into a context, such as splitting up candy between friends, might help students understand that 22 can't be the right answer. If we point out the difference between the incorrect and correct answers, they still might not know what caused the miscalculation. The reason for the error may represent more than a just procedural error; it may show a lack of understanding of what they are doing conceptually.

The example above shows how important it is to be precise in our teaching. We need to stress that numbers and procedures aren't just steps on paper but relate to real-world situations.

If it becomes apparent that a student's understanding of the place value system is lacking, we need to discern this and go that direction with our lesson. Tying mathematical concepts together is a constant requirement of teachers. Make it intentional and students will understand at deeper levels.

Explaining Word Meanings

Different terms for referencing a mathematical amount may make sense to us as adults, but for kids maybe not as much. An example is how society uses fractions, decimals and percentages as conventions for "parts of a whole." When helping students understand the use of different terms for similar concepts, I always use the same example of different names for the same person. One student may call her mother "Mom," but that same mom might also be called "sister," "daughter," "Margaret," or "Peg." Students then understand that for the same amount or quantity in math there may be different terms to name it depending on the way it is used.

Even when you think students already have an idea of what a term means, this might not be the case. While working with students on "reducing" or "simplifying" a fraction, it's very easy to begin work on the concept and not realize that the words themselves, and not just the concept, are unknown. I realized during one lesson that I had taken for granted that students understood "to reduce" meant to make something smaller and that "to simplify" meant to make something easier.

To explain what "reduce" meant, I drew two crazy profiles of a person, one with a beer belly (we are in Wisconsin after all) and one without. We talked about waistlines and how people on diets try to "reduce" their waistlines, or make them smaller. To explain why the process can also be called "simplifying," we talk about 1,000,000 slices of pizza on our school campus (Can you hear the students cheer at this thought?). I then mention that if students ate 500,000 slices one day, it would leave 500,000 slices leftover. While these are large numbers to use, and some students may have a hard time grasping them, that is exactly the point. As a group, we say out loud the fraction of 500,000/1,000,000 and recognize just how hard that fraction is to pronounce. We discuss that 500,000 is really just one half a million, so why not just call it that? One half sure is a lot easier to say. I explain this is why we reduce and simplify; the numbers are easier to use and it's more like the way we speak in everyday life.

> When learning to connect coordinate pairs of
> (2,3), (8,1) and (6,8) on an X-Y grid,
> *"If we flip-flopped the numbers,*
> *would the shape look the same but opposite?"*
> McKenna, 4th grader

This quote is a perfect example of gaining insight into student thinking. Stop and imagine what was going on in her young mind for her to ask a probing question like that. She must have been moving numbers around in her head, wondering how two number lines overlap each other or thinking of how lines connect to coordinates in different ways. I love hearing questions like that. They push me to think about things in new ways or in greater depth.

Metacognition for Instruction

Great math teaching involves being very metacognitive about how we solve problems as adults—what are we thinking, step by step? We actually think in minor steps that add up to solving problems. Being able to describe our thinking is very helpful to students.

Let's take a look at a procedural example: $\frac{1}{8} + \frac{3}{4} = ?$

I model my thinking to students for this problem, and here it is:

1. I notice it's a fraction problem where the answer is the unknown.

2. The procedure is addition.

3. I recall what is needed in fraction addition problems: they need common denominators, and numerators are added together but not denominators.

4. Are the denominators the same?

5. If the denominators are different, can one of them be multiplied to equal the other one?

6. If so, then just change one denominator by multiplying it by a factor to equal the other denominator. Use the same factor to multiply the numerator, also.

7. If one denominator cannot be easily changed to the other, find what could possibly be the common denominator using the least common multiple of the denominators.

8. Change both fractions to have same denominators by multiplying them by required factors.

9. Add numerators and keep the same denominator for the answer.

There is an entire, logical flow chart of steps involved in my thinking. This flow of steps comes to me instinctively, and does to some students, too. But it may not come that way to many other students, which is why we have to be metacognitive and explicitly teach these steps to students. Other examples are within us, if we really think about them. How about adding $8 + 7 + 2 = 17$? Do we do $8 + 2 = 10$ and then add the 7 to make 17? If so, then share this strategy with students explicitly.

In this chapter, I've tried to give a glimpse into ways to "see" what kids are thinking and just a few examples of what it means to teach explicitly. The approaches to use, and teachable moments in which to use them, are too serendipitous to cover in a chapter of a book. A discerning teacher who is aware and open to these moments is a teacher who can blow kids away with learning. Just imagine all the questions in the minds of the students we work with. By digging deeper into students' thinking, and meeting them with explicit instruction, we will get their learning to explode.

Here's a small sampling of actual questions from fourth graders in the last couple of years:

1. Is 3.88.037 a valid number?

2. Can there be remainders with decimal numbers?

3. Can we divide fractions by decimal numbers?

4. Can there be a fraction on top of a fraction?

5. How can there be a 200%?

6. Can you use a continuous symbol with whole numbers?

7. Can you have $^3/_4$ or .75 continuous?

8. Can you have more than two things that are parallel?

9. What is $-5^2 + 6$?

Chapter 11

Using Student Ideas

While playing a game with fake money,
and after she was fined for "excessive whining":
"Here's a dollar to pay ahead for my next two whines!"
Isabella, 4th grader

Our students' minds are a wonder. They are full of refreshing ideas, altruistic dreams, and broad perspectives. Don't we all enjoy the imagination of children? I sometimes stand in awe as I hear and watch students interact. Children bring a special energy and creativity into the classroom. They also bring crazy ideas. And while we can't use all the ideas brought up in class, I find it a thrill to take a child's creativity announced in class and integrate it into a math lesson. This chapter offers just a sample of the ideas shared by students, making the classroom and their learning their own.

Raising the Roof

"Mr. Wilson, can we 'Raise the Roof?!'" That's the question that came from several students after we completed a lesson dealing with integers. They were excited to gain a new understanding and they wanted to celebrate. Since the lesson was given with a small group in our computer lab, I asked them if they could do it with a whisper instead. They were okay with that. Here they are, in unison, as they stood on chairs, whispering, "Raise the Roof, Raise the Roof, Raise the Roof." This one-minute celebration of learning at the end of a lesson was a way to take their enthusiasm and use it to promote math even more.

Ice Cream Cones

While practicing the use of the long division bracket in her math notebook, one student noticed how the problem under the bracket got thinner and thinner as she progressed toward the answer. She raised her hand to announce that the problem looked like an ice cream cone. Thus, the idea of drawing ice cream cones around division problems was created. From that point on in the lesson, while students practiced more problems, each new problem in notebooks turned into a new, colorful ice cream cone. This idea offered by a student turned a mundane task of practicing division problems into a creative, enthusiastic endeavor. And as I made my way around the room, checking and correcting where needed, students displayed their cones, and told me which flavor they had created. Some even said they would add cherries to the ice cream to represent the remainder or wanted gelato instead of ice cream! Yes, ideas can come of out of nowhere.

Will's Superpig

At the end of the school year, it can almost seem that we've seen it all from our students. I've learned that is never the case. To introduce the concept of subtracting a negative number, we had a discussion about double negatives in grammar. On the Smartboard, I wrote a sentence such as, "Joe did not not go home." I then asked students if they thought Joe did or did not go home, according to the sentence. Some students didn't initially see the logic used to decide if Joe went home or not, but they caught on. According to the sentence, Joe actually did go home. (If he did the opposite of *not* going home, he must have gone home.) As a class, we discussed how this double negative is frowned upon in writing because it is very confusing; it's just too hard to follow. We then transferred the idea of double negative to a math problem such as 8 − (-2) where it turns into 8 + 2. Mathematically, if we subtract the opposite of a number, we must add the number.

As we went through this concept, I wondered if several students really understood how to do the procedure. One boy raised his hand to announce that he had come up with a way to remember, and asked if he could he come up to draw his idea. I thought, "Why not?" He came to the Smartboard and went on to draw his "Superpig," who was soaring above two negatives fighting each other and then would come down to save them and turn things positive.

We all had quite a laugh at the creation of his new superhero, but it made sense. While the underlying math property still may have needed to be presented more thoroughly, kids got the procedure. If I had prevented that boy from demonstrating his idea because I was hurried or flustered, the idea might never have been shared. By giving him the opportunity to share his idea, it gave me a glimpse into his thinking, and it also was a fun way to help other students who may not have understood the concept completely. I never would have thought to mix in a superhero with this problem. It's also a good example to all students that their thinking may be different than mine or others, and that is okay, and it's worthy.

Stop Motion Project

Not all student ideas are small, off-the-cuff moments. Some have been simmering for a long time. As one school year wound down, I came up with new ways for sixth grade math students to demonstrate their learning. I suggested several options for students, including Powerpoint projects, short skits, mock game shows, videos and more. Students loved the idea of being creative in their final projects. As students left the room at the end of the period, one girl approached me to ask, "Mr. Wilson, I've always wanted to make a stop-motion video. Can I do that?" My response is pretty obvious by now, right? To accomplish the goal of finishing student-created projects over the last ten days of math class, part of each class was reserved for student projects. Around the room, small groups worked diligently to make their projects just right. Off to the side, this girl did her own thing with a digital camera, a pair of scissors and a stack of construction paper. By the end of the school year, students had created some outstanding projects. None were better than hers, and I still have a copy of it on my computer. To complete the project, she took over 1,200 photos!

Because I gave her an opportunity to use an idea she had been pondering for years, this student created a project that let her express herself and her thinking, and also created another way for other students to see math in action. This project wasn't just me standing in front of class leading a math lesson—it was a student leading. Learning can come at any time in the process. This way of presenting quite possibly could have made the difference in another student's understanding.

Qbert and MiniMum

Another student idea originated within a long division lesson. I told students the term for the answer to a division problem started with a "Q," so a discussion was opened up for possible answers. One of the first guesses was "Qbert." All the class chuckled and agreed that "Qbert" would be a good way to remember the "Q" that starts the real answer of "quotient." It was as easy as that.

One Thanksgiving, my girlfriend Kim and I traveled to South Dakota to see the Badlands, Custer State Park and Mount Rushmore. While on the trip, I bought a small stuffed buffalo. Since the class had studied Native Americans earlier in the year, including the Plains Indians who depended heavily on buffalo, I thought it would be a fun addition to class. After the trip I showed students the buffalo, and all agreed that the buffalo should be named "Qbert." From that point on, "Qbert" became our class mascot, and connected students to math.

Later in the year, I was fortunate enough to travel to an annual conference of independent schools in Orlando, Florida. (When I was approached and asked if I'd like to leave Wisconsin in mid-winter to travel to Florida, it didn't take long to agree!) While in a workshop during the conference, a group from Disney led a demonstration on using animal videos to teach science. At the end of the workshop, the presenters raffled off the stuffed animals used in the activity, and I won a small stuffed bear. Of course, I brought it back to class and presented it to be part of our classroom. At that time, students were working with statistical terms such as minimum, maximum, range, mean, median and mode. As we were discussing minimum, a student interjected that the bear could be "MiniMum" and be married to "Qbert." From that point on, that was her name!

These are just a few of the student-led ideas that have enhanced the classroom. None of them took away from the learning in the class, but rather, enriched it. While teachers may not have time to allow for every student idea to be presented, we must at least allow for flexibility within lessons. The creativity demonstrated by our students during the learning process is incredible. Each year, teaching and learning in my classroom evolves to create something beyond my plan. Students are filled with ideas to help make learning fun and engaging; we just have to listen and be open to them. And the room may just end up with a class mascot.

Chapter 12

Creative Engagement

"Does infinity – 6 = negative infinity?"
Peter, 4th grader

Sometimes teachers wonder if students are really connecting with what happens in class. The following story proves that they are. While at an after-school track meet for several students of mine, I ended up talking with a parent of one student. Suddenly, three or four of the students ran up and pulled me and the mother to the side of the track. One of them had been talking with her skeptical older brother about how fun math class was, and wanted to show him the math dance they were learning in class. So, here we were, watching fourth graders perform a math dance for the brother, at a track meet. These were engaged students connecting with what was going on in the classroom!

To advance students as far as I can while they're with me takes both an understanding of where they are with their knowledge and ability, and lessons that have substance. No matter the goal of my math lessons, I try to take into account students' engagement; are they intent on learning or are they dozing off or thinking about recess? That's the reason I do my best to include joy, movement or talking as part of a lesson. This isn't a new concept, but the design has to be intentional. The strategies used to accomplish this are many.

In my math class, students learn quickly that we don't mess around; students *know* they will be involved, so they better be ready. There's no time to waste, but there is time to have fun within the lesson. Sometimes the math classroom takes on the look of comedy improvisation on stage, while at other times it may look very studious. The class comes to have a good balance of rigor and enjoyment, by design.

One thing we do is use the physical space around us whenever we can, whether it involves staying in the room or not. Instead of using the book to discuss polygons and just going through the appropriate pages and problems, we look around the room and point out different types and have a discussion. Students notice and want to share.

When we can we get out of the classroom, students may end up wandering the hallways with metric rulers looking for items of a certain length, or they might explore the building looking for arrays. Students are challenged to find things in the building they think no one else will see—specific lengths of window sills, angles of tiles on the floor, or arrays such as the columns and rows within a window screen, lights on the ceiling, or tables arranged in the cafeteria. This gets students out of their seats and engaged. We then come back to the classroom to discuss their findings. The activities are not just for fun, but have a focused goal. If I didn't allow students to share what they found, the lesson would be lacking. This discussion portion is very important; it gets their exploration out of just their heads in only a mental state, but out in the open as a social interaction.

When teaching about adding integers:
"When using positive and negative numbers, what is zero?"
Will, 4th grader

Another way to get kids engaged is by asking them to do simple things in a fun way, like the way they pronouce decimal numbers. Instead of using worksheets to skill and drill repeatedly, numbers with varying degrees of difficulty are listed on the board. Students are then asked to pick a number they're comfortable with, and say the number in a sophisticated way ("nine and three tenths") and also the shortcut way ('nine point three"). This verbal approach connects them to the process, but doesn't put too much pressure on them because of the different levels on the board.

Students need to learn the meaning of "and" and not just "point" in a decimal number. Teachers need to make sure kids really understand what the difference is because knowing what the "and" means brings understanding. In this case, "and" means we're adding a portion of a number onto the whole number. One way to check understanding is to use the decimal number .4, and see if students pronounce the number, "and four tenths."

Students may not know that they don't need to use the "and" when there is no whole number. These are small, explicit details that help students understand our adult systems.

In addition to pronouncing decimal numbers in two ways, we also pick a number to say three times as fast as we can without flubbing it up. This becomes a fun way for kids to use the numbers out loud, and gets all involved. If they flub up, and most do, so what? Everyone knows we're laughing with them, not at them. Sometimes students are asked to whisper, talk as an old person, yell or sing the number, while at other times it's done in "slow-motion" or hummed for a change of pace. If the number was "nine and three-tenths" they would hum "mmm, mmm mmm-mmm." This turns the activity into group fun. Think about the short time it takes to do this, yet this simple activity can be so much fun for kids.

The fun in a classroom must be matched with explicit instruction and rigorous thought. Just recently, we revisited decimal numbers using the problem 10 + 1.8. On the board, I purposely didn't write the digits in vertical format, but wrote out the problem horizontally. Almost every student answered 2.8, not lining up the place values (tens, units, and tenths) I thought they already knew how to use. Instead, most students just lined up digits, not caring about place value or the decimal point. It was a somewhat frustrating and surprising moment. I want students to connect things we do in class, but sometimes they don't do it automatically. I realized I had not been explicit enough to help students make the necessary connections.

In this chapter I stress being explicit in instruction, but there are also times I don't teach things explicitly. This is intentional because I want to see what students can do without me. In this case, it was obvious in student responses that most did not connect the numbers in the addition problem (10 + 1.8) to something they had been doing all year long. They had been comparing indoor and outdoor temperatures all year long, using a temperature gauge (to the tenth degree) found at Gander Mountain, but the practice didn't transfer to other problems automatically. In another case, most students could add $5 + .25 to get $5.25, but when the money connection was removed, it seemed as if their logic in the numbers disappeared, leading many to add them incorrectly.

As you can see, although most things I do in class result in good learning, it's not always the case. Constant self-evaluation of instruction is very important. Most of the time, my instruction is explicit, but I don't want my students to get used to being spoon-fed everything they need to learn and depend on me too much. I often have to ponder my approach and adjust. Here again is the importance of balance. I want them to think for themselves and work through mistakes, but also want to push them in a supportive way.

While looking at a tall isosceles triangle
being drawn on the board,
"Does it have to be that tall?"
Peter, 4th grader

"Do they have two same angles, too?"
Isabella, 4th grader

Engagement involves the right amount of challenge, differentiation and keeping kids on their toes, all in a positive way. The thing to do is put ourselves in students' shoes, and then really expand our thinking to see how the things they are being taught can be taken to new levels. I am always trying to think of how adults use what students are learning. As adults, no one comes up to us in a grocery store and asks us, "If two trains are traveling in opposite directions, when will they meet?" But how *do* adults use math? We use it dealing with our finances, building models or homes, quilting, keeping our speed just above the speed limit while driving, talking about the statistics of different sports teams, measuring the right amount of chocolate chips in a recipe, and so forth. And we rarely use math in a vacuum of one operation or one concept. Students need to be continually exposed to this overlap of concepts. In lower grades, they may not become experts at the nuances of math, but they need to know that math is everywhere.

Can we do away with repeated use of procedures to make sure kids understand the steps to solve problems? Probably not, and

I'm just as guilty as the next guy at getting kids to be good at procedures. But can we please get them to understand why they are important in their future? Knowing math procedures is important so students can be successful in more advanced classes. Having math sense is important for being able to discern what is needed to solve problems. And all of it is important so students can be mathematically literate as adults, when reading articles, problem-solving, and calculating everyday math situations that they will encounter. Will they always have a calculator with them to figure out a 15-20% tip at a restaurant? In our current time of smart phones, maybe they will. But I don't want to send my students out into the world only depending on the technology at hand to be able to operate in our world. Even if they do depend on it, I want them to understand the process and reason for their answers.

Students recently used calculators in class to help with adding the decimal-numbered temperatures of cities they were tracking. The goal was to sum up the different temperatures and then find the average or mean. Since most students didn't have the overall working knowledge of dividing decimal numbers (in fourth grade), they were allowed to use calculators for the activity. Some students correctly punched in the numbers and got the correct answers. Most made mistakes as they punched in the numbers and came up with answers that made no sense. Some of them recognized this, but some did not. This activity gave students a good example of why people cannot depend on calculators or technology in general. What if they were on the wrong end of an error in a store or they made the error themselves, and it cost them or another person some money? Might that make a difference to someone? You bet they agreed with that.

Okay, so creative engagement is a big deal, but how does that translate from being a goal to a consistent aspect of a classroom? Engagement doesn't just happen and it has to be a more than a goal; it has to be a mission, an internal desire, a determined persistence, to blow students away, inspiring them to love learning.

Take a look at the different approaches included in this chapter. Some of these approaches are games, but engagement entails much more than games. Implement just a few of these approaches, and students may just start loving math class.

> *"If there are parallelograms,*
> *how come there aren't perpendicularograms?"*
> Red, 4th grader

Array Bridge

During one semester, while I was using a spare classroom for math lessons, the school's maintenance crew decided to move a long bulletin board into the same room. For the first few days, students worked around the bulletin board lying on the floor. Then one morning I decided to *use* the board instead of letting it be an annoyance. Since we were dealing with the area of arrays (a combination of rows and columns), we used the board to represent the gap between two cliffs. Students were divided into two teams, each on one end of the bulletin board, and I assigned them the task of using small, paper arrays to create one bridge to connect the two cliffs. To make it harder, obstacles were placed at strategic spots on the board for teams to maneuver around. Before they started connecting the two portions of the bridge, I also told them to be prepared to be asked individually (and at random times) to show me the area of a portion of the bridge.

This activity turned into a loud, active, team-building math tradition that I use every year. And it gave students the opportunity to find areas of rectangles (say 8 cm by 10 cm) using actual grid paper, instead of looking at one in a book. They could handle the arrays, all while being challenged and having fun. This gave them a chance to see how larger or longer arrays looked differently from others, and how the area of shapes could be manipulated in a variety of ways.

The Stunt

Growing up in Wisconsin made me a huge fan of the Green Bay Packers. (Go Pack Go!) An old friend of mine invited me to a Monday Night Football game during the school year, but I hesitated because it was going to take a lot of driving to and from the game, after a long day of school. I told her I wasn't twenty-four years old anymore and couldn't handle crazy hours, but she wasn't about to let that excuse work. So, on that scheduled Monday, I drove thirty miles to teach a full day of school to my fourth graders, then drove one hundred and twenty miles to Green Bay, watched the game and then drove another hundred miles back to my home in Milwaukee. It turned into a very long Monday, but the Packers destroyed the other team, so it was all worth it.

That night, when my friend and I entered Lambeau Field, we found folded cards attached to our seats to be used for a "stunt" during the national anthem. I learned that night that a "stunt" is when audience members in a stadium hold up cards at a certain time to create a design that can be seen from across or above the stadium.

The next morning I showed my students the stunt card and a photo I took of the stadium during the stunt. They were thrilled, and some of them even said they saw it on the broadcast the night before. Later that day, I pondered the math and organization involved in designing a stunt. The next day, we discussed the stunt in math class, and I asked students if they could design one. Their answer was a resounding, "Yes!"

Since my school has an all-school assembly in the theater every month, I contacted the theater director to see if she thought we could pull off a stunt during the next assembly, which was in three weeks. She said, "Go for it." Was this part of my planned units for math that year? No, but the opportunity presented itself, and it was a great learning event: fun and active. The next day, students scoped out the theater to plan the stunt and had to answer several questions. Should they do the stunt on the stage *for* the audience? Should they put cards on each seat for the audience to actually do the stunt? If paper is put on seats, will younger students play with the paper during the assembly? Should the stunt be recorded so the audience can see it? We tested certain lengths of paper and taped them to the back of seats. Then students sat in the seats and pulled up the paper at certain "go" commands. While I worked with students deciding how paper should be used, other students took it upon themselves to count the seats in each row—which were different lengths—to create a seating map. Since it was going to be a Christmas assembly, we decided to use plain white paper for certain seats and wrapping paper to create the stunt's image.

To accomplish the stunt, students thought of a design the audience could create and then figured out which seats should get which papers. Students did all of this by measuring, cutting, and then laying papers out in the music room behind the theater. As we did this, certain students had specific jobs: cutting, organizing or being part of the assembly line as we laid the paper sections out on the floor. As I directed which papers should be pulled for each row, one student caught a mistake and re-arranged how papers were ordered. He was engaged, and so were all the other students. As we went along, we realized we needed "Go" signs for three theater sections and "Happy Holidays" signs for the front row of students who would not have paper for the stunt. Another group of students made these signs. The night before the event, students taped each piece of paper to the back of a seat in the theater.

During the assembly, we knew we had five minutes to pull off the stunt, so several students and I directed from the stage. When all of the sections were ready, I took a panoramic photo that we projected later in the assembly. The stunt worked as planned, and here is the result—ULS spelled in the seats of the theater.

Think of the math, problem-solving, and organization involved in this project. Students used math to count the seats in each row and then figure out which seats should have white paper and which should have wrapping paper. They had to make sure to have even borders of white on each edge of each seating section. This was a complicated process, since we also wanted to make sure each of the letters in the stunt were of equal width. Students also had to discern the length of each piece of paper, and then measure and cut each sheet precisely. They also had to think of the time the entire stunt would take and how to plan the implementation of the entire process. If I was stuck with a textbook and a set curriculum, I would not have the freedom to bring ideas like this from a Packer game into my classroom.

Fear Factor Math

By far the most memorable activity in math class is Fear Factor Math. Every few months, students in my class play this game in small teams in a timed relay race. But it's not just any relay race—it's got math, speed and "iffy" food.

"Can we have a smelly cheese version?"
Many 4th graders

I set up the game by placing a page of multi-leveled math problems on each end of a table. Sandwiched between them are foods for participants to eat. Some of the foods chosen for this activity include beets, canned asparagus, broccoli, refried beans, wax beans, Spam, dried seaweed, mealworms, Brussels sprouts, and banana peppers. During a team's opportunity at the game, each teammate must solve one problem on the first sheet, and then eat a spoonful of a "challenging" food. Students must chew and show they've swallowed their food choice before moving on to the second page full of math problems. When they have completed one problem from the second page, they tag their teammate to continue the relay. Once a food choice has been used, it is eliminated from other teammates' choices; the last teammate has no choice but to eat whatever food is left. Since the game is a timed activity, each incorrect math answer adds two seconds to the team's total time.

Students are not required to be part of the relay team. If students choose not to be eaters, they may work as scorekeepers, verify answers or keep time. And although students rarely spit anything out, if a food is too horrible for participants to swallow, they may spit it out into a garbage can.

One surprising result of playing this game is that banana peppers became such a hit, students began asking their parents to buy them at the grocery store. One girl even brought them for her morning snack. And if I bring banana peppers into the cafeteria, kids always walk over to my table to beg for one. Suddenly, practicing math procedures was something students looked forward to doing. What started as a way to make reviewing math facts more tolerable ended up introducing students to experiences and flavors that carried over into their lives outside the classroom.

The game has also become a tradition when grandparents are invited to school for their special day. Not only do our guests watch Fear Factor Math, but they also join the fun with their grandchildren. They help solve math problems, and they eat the same foods as the students. It is a real hoot watching grandparents join students in eating Spam or beets, and they love playing along. (And no, no grandparents have had to spit out any food!)

After playing Fear Factor Math,
*"I hope my dentist doesn't see
the mealworm crumbs in my mouth
when I go see him later!"*
Gloria, 4th grader

Using Polygons

While my students learn about polygons, they also get to play. If a visitor walked into the room during this lesson, they might think it was too much fun. But getting students excited about polygons rarely comes from just using a textbook. In this lesson, students use plastic triangles to make designs, some symmetrical, some abstract, some even create scenes with palm trees. This doesn't involve a lot of number-crunching, yet still includes a lot of visual math and decision-making, even if students don't think about it. In a lesson leading up to our "play" day, students used protractors to measure various angles in their designs.

In a more advanced challenge, students are required to create cities with arrays for sidewalks and streets, and with a specific number of 2D polygons and circles for buildings. As they do this in groups, they are required to find the area of each shape they use. For even more advanced students, groups are required to use at least a few 3D shapes and find the volume of each shape. Most groups put tremendous effort into the design of their cities. Other groups create castles, airports, malls, playgrounds, parks or downtown street scenes. The ownership students feel for their creations demonstrates just how engaged students are when they can use their hands and imaginations to work with polygons and other shapes.

Crazy Socks

As I mentioned earlier in the book, when I first thought of becoming a teacher, one perk I imagined was never wearing a tie to work ever again. As I thought about introducing students to probability, I thought of wearing a tie once per week, and having students guess which day it would happen. On Fridays, students guessed which day the following week I would wear the tie and recorded it as either $^1/_5$, 1:5 or one out of five (for a five day week) on their entry card. The activity doesn't include intense instruction, yet it has an intentional purpose. While some students may not immediately understand the different ways to write out probability, they do understand the concept of representing a certain portion of a larger amount. I wanted this activity to be another subconscious learning system we could use the entire year. Later, when we do work more specifically on probability, students have this prior knowledge of the different representations.

After receiving hamburger-designed crazy socks to wear,
"Can I taste them? Are they scratch and sniff?"
Mason, 4th grader

My initial idea of wearing a tie just did not cut it; I *had* to find something more comfortable than a tie. That's when crazy socks jumped into my mind. First, I found some bright turquoise socks. Then, my co-teacher bought me two more pairs for Christmas: a red pair with lightning bolts and a pair with mustaches. Since starting this idea, I've received so many crazy socks from students that the system has been modified. Students now guess which day I will *not* wear crazy socks. And now, when students see me in the morning, many come over to lift the hem of my pants to see if they picked the correct day. On the day I wear plain socks, we review all of the guesses at the morning meeting; students with incorrect guesses get a friendly death stare and winners win a small prize. It may seem very simplistic, but it helps students get excited about probability.

Receiving the gift of hamburger socks

Karaoke, with Dancing Option

One of my goals is for students to be able to consistently verbalize their mathematical thinking. I use a karaoke project to help with this, by giving students the option of writing math vocabulary into appropriate songs. Not only does this get students to think about which math terms to use and how to describe them, but they end up saying or singing the terms multiple times. Students are also required to create a companion Powerpoint presentation so others can see the lyrics and sing along.

In two separate schools, this karaoke experiment took other turns. In addition to using math terms for the lyrics and creating Powerpoint slideshows, students choreographed dance steps to match the lyrics they created. To finish their projects in class and still continue our progress in math, the first half of class was dedicated to instruction, while the second half was reserved for development of their song projects. This wasn't a long process; practice and design took only five or six class periods.

At each school, students performed their song and dance in front of others. During the live performances, students performed once and then asked the audience to join in the second time around. One performance was in front of 3-8 graders in the school's gym, while the other was in front of the whole K-12 school during an all-school assembly in the school theater. Watching other students follow along as they sang and danced was quite a thrill for all of us. I also carefully watched how some teachers responded to the surprise math performance. Not all teachers or administrators are going to agree with the reasoning behind such a performance; they may not see the advantages it provides, or they may come from more traditional backgrounds. At the first school, I sensed that some teachers watching the kids dancing didn't quite appreciate the idea of performing a "dance party" as part of math instruction. These teachers seemed lukewarm at best to having their students watch or participate in the dance. But, that didn't stop me from using it again.

Using activities like these helps students connect to math; there is a wealth of research that proves the more senses a student can use when learning a subject, the better that student will retain what they have learned. When students participate in something like the karaoke project, they are using many senses: they are writing out their math terms, they are saying and singing their math terms, they are hearing their classmates sing their own math songs, they are seeing the math terms written out in Powerpoint slides, and they are moving their bodies in time to the beat.

This past spring, a student reminded me how much long-term learning occurs when students creatively use all of their senses to engage a certain topic. A student I taught two years ago approached me and I asked what we were doing in math class.

As we talked, she went on to show me the dance moves and words to the math song her class had created. Her class had connected math vocabulary with movements that were designed to represent concepts from geometry—for example, the movement for "obtuse angles" in the song involved forming an angle larger than 90 degrees with her arms. She remembered every bit of math her class had included in their song. This type of activity *does* make a difference.

Mathingo

Another game we consistently play is "Mathingo," a combination of bingo and math. Students' game boards are made with standard size paper, but with large protractors copied onto them. I do this intentionally because most students have limited use with protractors. To create different sections on their game boards, students are required to draw lines from the vertex of the large protractor to create angles of 30, 60, 90, 120 and 150 degrees. This creates sliced sections of the protractor where students write their choice of several different products (answers to multiplication problems). Students use a pair of dice (one die numbered 1-6, the other die numbered 5-10) to practice multiplication facts while playing the game. The numbers from each roll become a pair of factors students multiply to form a product. If they have that product on their game board, they can cover that section with a chip. Other sets of dice can be created, too, to help students practice other math operations. By using the copied protractors as game boards, students build prior knowledge of using a vertex and angles. This helps later in the year when students begin using protractors to measure and draw angles.

When students cover enough spots on their game boards to win a game, they need to yell "Mathingo." When we first started playing the game, students asked what they could win. In our class, students don't win points or candy; they win exploding fist-pumps from the teacher, and that's about it. Yes, fourth graders are easy to please! Sometimes, if kids say "Bingo" instead of "Mathingo" when they win, they need to do five pushups or sit-ups. This is another example of how much students want to be active—they will do exercises that aren't even required!

Exponential Growth

Another game we play explains exponential growth in a fun way. I ask students to write down sixty-four of their favorite foods. Then I ask them to get in groups of six, with each person responsible for speaking for ten seconds of a one-minute time limit. One person announces only two of his or her favorite foods in the first ten seconds, the second person shares four foods in the next ten seconds, the third person says eight in the next ten seconds, and so forth. By the time students get to the sixth ten-second segment, that last student is trying to say sixty-four food items in ten seconds. It's hilarious to watch kids try this. After playing the activity once, all kids want to be the one trying to say sixty-four foods in ten seconds, so we play the game several times. This game quickly drives home the concept of exponential growth in a memorable way, with lots of laughs besides.

Pi Day on March 14ᵗʰ (3.14)

Many schools have a Pi contest on March 14th where students memorize as many digits of Pi as they can (3.1415...). In my classroom, this day is a big event for another reason, too— March 14th is my birthday. I always wear my Pi t-shirt and I encourage students to also wear numbered clothing. My approach on this day is more involved than just having students regurgitate digits of Pi. I want my students to understand what Pi is and how it is used, with a little mystery involved.

Pi equals the circumference of a circle divided by its diameter. This works for every circle on earth, and it still amazes me. The activity we use is designed to prove that Pi works even if students are in the dark until the end of the activity. Instead of telling students what Pi means, I have them measure different sized circular objects such as can tops, compact discs, and such. After explaining circumference and diameter, students use tape measures to figure out good ways to measure lengths of items they choose. I tell them there is no need to be perfectly precise, but it helps if they are. Some students figure out it's easier to measure circumference by marking one spot on an item and then rolling it over a flattened tape measure. Others try their best to wrap a tape measure around their object, being as accurate as possible. For each item they measure, students are asked to record both circumference and diameter measurements on the whiteboard.

After students have measured and recorded several items, I ask them to divide the circumference of their items by their diameter. Since they are in fourth grade and haven't been exposed to dividing decimals numbers, we use calculators for this part. As they do this exercise, they find out most of their answers are somewhat close to 3.14. And if they aren't, it means their measuring was a bit inaccurate or they used the calculators incorrectly. Then I ask them to look at the number for Pi. When they see that their answers are close to Pi, many want to re-measure to be more accurate, with excitement in their voices and on their faces.

This activity is filled with many goals—students learning about Pi, students feeling excited to prove how a number is used, and students getting a chance to discuss accuracy.

Who Wants to be Math Wizard?

Many students struggle to describe the math they know. In this game, I ask students to create questions ahead of time by reviewing their math journals. They need to create math questions that are relevant to the math they've studied and in various levels of difficulty. By doing it this way, students look at the different math concepts learned throughout the year. This game is played in pairs and the goal is to reach the top of a staircase I draw on the board. Participants must talk and solve problems together, but just like the television show *Who Wants to be a Millionaire*, they have lifelines to use if they are stuck on a problem. They may ask a friend for help or phone an expert, who happens to be me. The audience is also involved in the game, since they must also do the problems. Kids love this game because they can be with a partner, and can also ask for help without embarrassment. If they make the top stair (and usually they do), they win a genuine acknowledgment of their accomplishment.

Up and Down

During an interview for a teaching job many years ago, I was required to design and implement my view of a typical fourth grade math lesson. Since fractions are a big deal in elementary school, I decided to go that route with the lesson. I started the lesson by asking, "How many students are in the class?" We got the answer, "Twenty." I next asked, "How many of you like chocolate chip mint ice cream?" Eighteen of the twenty said they liked that flavor, so I asked them to stand. The answer to the next question was telling, as I asked, "How does this example relate to fractions?"

As the class discussed the idea, we discovered that the initial number of students, all of whom had stayed seated, was the denominator of a fraction. This then led us to realize that the number of students who stood in answer to the chocolate chip mint question were actually the numerator of a fraction ($^{18}/_{20}$). After developing this awareness, students wanted to keep asking different questions to engage with the lesson. This up and down movement got students moving in the math lesson, and was the impetus for yet another game I use in class.

In this game, all students learn a set of body gestures relating to math terms that I project onto a screen or that I write on large cards. Students may fold their hands to demonstrate a "product," while they may hold their hands apart for "factors." To start the game, all students stand up and then must react to the different terms I show them. To stay standing, they must quickly say the term as they move to correctly gesture, without looking at others, and without flinching to do a different gesture. If they are too slow, do not say the term or do the wrong gesture, they must sit down. The last couple of students standing are declared the winners. Whenever we play this game, just one try is never enough. I also use this game for other subjects; we've just made up gestures for the non-mathematical terms we want to study.

National Park Project

I love going to national parks and have been traveling to them for adventure and outdoor photography for many years. Seeing the natural beauty of our nation always inspires me. Along the way, I've collected many park guides, which include information on one side, and a map of the park on the other. Any national park, monument, seashore, or wildlife refuge within the National Park Service has its own park guide with the same layout. Whether it's Zion and Bryce Canyon National Parks in Utah, Grand Teton National Park in Wyoming, or Olympic National Park in Washington, the information is usually relevant to something we are studying in class, and the natural beauty depicted is stunning.

As a way to introduce students to the allure of the parks and create a unit to integrate several subjects, I created the National Park Project. Students research different aspects of many locations. Within this research, they use the guides, but they also use the Internet to find information such as the annual attendance, square mileage and elevation of their locations. This project is designed for students to use fractions, decimal numbers and percentages in a way that adults might if they were writing a travel article. By requiring students to grapple with large numbers in several ways, their understanding of different uses for numbers expands.

Students are required to study a minimum of five national parks and compare them according to a particular set of aspects, using a graphic organizer I provide them. They must use their research to create graphs in Excel and a narrative using Word or Powerpoint. As an extension of the main project, I give students basic specification sheets from stores like an R.E.I. These sheets list information for outdoor gear, such as tents, hiking books, or freeze-dried food, and include prices, weights, heights, and volume quantities. Students are given an imaginary amount of money for a budget and the task of planning a three- to four-day "camping" trip using the specification sheets to buy their "gear." To make it a bit more fun, students are able to research while sitting in a tent setup in the classroom.

Miscellaneous Ideas

Other ways I creatively engage students are: having students creating their own videos such as a mock "American Idol" math contest or "Jeopardy" game show, keeping statistics on shooting hoops into a paper basket with recycled paper, or using educational games from the school's textbook. Since almost every textbook has games and activities, my hope is that teachers don't dismiss the importance of these games and how to use them to inspire real learning. Using store-bought games such as "Catch Phrase" or "Apples to Apples" is another idea; these games can be modified to match classroom needs. Even finding a floor space for students to form different types of triangles using their bodies can be a great idea. The evidence is clear—creating engaging ways for students to connect with math is really unlimited.

The games and activities I use don't emphasize competition, but instead emphasize play and numbers. Good sportsmanship is modeled and expected. The games also don't pin players against each other in a negative way, but rather let kids help each other to talk about the math that's taking place in their minds. Not every game is perfect, but kids look forward to these fun days.

One game I do shy away from is the "Around the World" game where kids compete against each other one on one to name a product from flashcards as fast as they can. While this game does provide practice in multiplication facts, the game lends itself only to quick-thinking math students, and doesn't do much to help struggling math students.

The fun and camaraderie games can provide are also invaluable and can be serendipitous. Here's an example. While students played a game to help them learn to give change to the nearest quarter, we used a spinner to find out which students would buy or sell an item. At other times, students would get an unexpected expense or deposit. As we played, I spontaneously added an aspect that made the game go from fun to hilarious. (Here I might say again that a visitor entering my classroom might see odd and seemingly unfocused work, but that wouldn't be the truth of things.) I had found a spinner on a math website that let me adjust the probability of each event. So, to add some spice to the game, some spaces on the spinner required students to do five sit-ups, squeal like a pig, or hop like a kangaroo (their suggestions). By using this adjustable spinner, students were able to follow how chances can change depending on different variables. The students loved it, yet learned about probability and how to make change with coins. It also left them wanting more of the game. And yes, the classroom got quite loud!

These activities prove that math instruction can be dynamic and active, even crazy at times. All of these games are not just for fun. It may seem like time is being wasted, but that's farthest from the truth. The connections students are making, and the joy they are having in math class, carry over into their boosted engagement and a greater willingness to practice math in a fun way. With determined planning, focused goals and creativity, students can become not only great mathematicians, but also have great fun along the way. Why not try it?

Banana Peppers Summary

I've described many different options to use in math instruction. Sometimes the fun approach to teaching subjects doesn't accomplish the deep thinking I expected. When this happens, I can adjust. I may notice that a game really made a difference with one concept, while an active project made a difference with another concept. As teachers learn to discern and adjust, they go from being active teachers to effective teachers, because students' learning will go from superficial to extremely deep.

Afterword

What to do with all of this?

Obviously, the goal of teaching is student learning; but if we ourselves don't plan on learning daily, we're in the wrong profession. Since we are dealing with young minds, we can never know where the teachable moments may occur, for them and for us.

When I had the first inkling to teach, one of the things I was looking forward to was being an expert in a field. In my last corporate job as a technical writer, I always felt I was semi-qualified; I never received any formal training in the field. While working in that position, I often had a secret, insecure feeling that I was writing about things I didn't really understand totally—and it was a feeling I didn't enjoy.

When I decided to get into teaching, I thought I'd go through education classes and finally feel I had the foundation and expertise to be someone who knew what he was doing. I expected a gut feeling of security in my knowledge. If I am brutally honest, I do have some secure feelings when things are really flowing, but there are also times where the schooling and preparation I've had as a teacher escape me.

Although the security I was expecting is fleeting at times, the teaching field has also given me the chance to learn every day.

At times, it's overwhelming how much a teacher can learn, and I've had to learn to accept that. A willingness to open myself up, while trusting myself to be capable, keeps me growing. Whether it's in a content area, keeping up with students' natural energy, working with parents, managing a class, designing lessons or working with colleagues, vulnerability is something teachers have to get used to, be real about, and be mature about. Is that always easy? No. But the learning comes if we are patient and open.

> While walking with a student down the hallway,
> Me: "Okay, if you were acting like a teacher,
> say something 'teacherish'."
> Student: "I love chocolate!"
> Caroline, 4th grade

What do we bring with us to teaching? Have we traveled? What do we know? Have we played sports? Have we conquered fears? What talents do we have? Bring it all to our teaching. Share stories, too. Weave it all into our teaching. And remember, not all great teachers started out as great teachers. Not all great teachers know how to handle every situation right away. Not all great teachers are calm all the time. And not all great teachers feel they're great.

Greatness comes with hard work, focus and determination to be the best for our students. In times of trial and challenge, our conviction will be tested. We must find it in us to persevere and let *nothing* get in the way of our mission. We need to go after it with everything we've got. We need to pour our hearts and souls into helping students to be the best they can be. That is our job and mission.

References

Jonas, P. (2014) A Funny thing happened on the way to the classroom. *Strich Magazine (Winter)*. p.15.

O'Keefe, C. (October, 2002). *EdM 512, Developmental Literacy PreK –Primary*, Lecture given at Cardinal Stritch University, Milwaukee, WI.

Perry, L. (2001). *Get This Party Started*, [Recorded by Pink]. On Missundaztood [CD]. New York, NY: Arista.

Sher, B. (1995). *I Could Do Anything If Only I Knew What It Was*. New York, NY: Random House.

Acknowledgments

I am very grateful to my family, Marlene, Kathi and David Wilson, and Carrie Massey, for their unconditional support of my teaching career. Thank you also to Kim for all of our listening sessions and for believing in all I do. My teaching career has blossomed because of many others: I would like to thank Dr. Corey Thompson for his enduring belief in my ideas, Rita and Cara Lewis for their help at RMS, Mark Horowitz for his effective modeling while student-teaching, my friends Loni, Randy, John, Tally and Holly for their enthusiastic support, teachers Carol Double, Jody Schneider, Jeff Cartier, Erin Sittig and Carolyn Rubenzer for their optimism and positivity, my ULS colleagues and all other teachers I've worked with who have made my job easier, and the many parents who have stood up for me and provided needed affirmation, especially early in my career. I'd also like to thank Jeff Eggert for his integrity and his support at the end of my corporate life. Also, I am grateful to my editor, Sue Fair, for her invaluable input in helping to make this manuscript worthy, and to Jane Marcussen, my cover designer, for making it fun and inviting. And finally, I'd like to thank all of my students along the way for being such great teachers, with special thanks to Sophie Dempsey, Hailey Bethke, and Maddie Mahoney for their great cover artwork.

About the Author

Peter Wilson is a passionate elementary educator and the founder of the non-profit organization Imaginaction, Inc. After spending fifteen years in the corporate world, in engineering and as a technical writer, trainer, and desktop publisher, he changed careers mid-life and found his passion. The decision transformed his life. He has taught fourth through eighth grade students in several schools and environments: Montessori, Math Teacher Leader, private and public. He has also taught at the graduate level and in Liberia, Africa. Mr. Wilson has traveled with students to Olympic National Park, WA, the Boundary Waters Canoe Area of Minnesota, Washington, D.C., The Netherlands, and Denmark. He has a Master's of Arts in Teaching from Cardinal Stritch University, and currently teaches fourth grade at University Lake School, in Hartland, Wisconsin. He lives in Wauwatosa, Wisconsin, and loves travel, music, art and outdoor photography.

Contact Peter at: imaginactionwi@yahoo.com or visit http://peterjenningswilson.weebly.com/

18767520R00147

Made in the USA
Middletown, DE
20 March 2015